INTEGRATION, MEASURE
and PROBABILITY

UNIVERSITY MATHEMATICAL MONOGRAPHS

Editor

D. E. RUTHERFORD, D.Sc., Dr.Math.

Integration, Measure and Probability .. .. .. H. R. Pitt, Ph.D., F.R.S.

INTEGRATION, MEASURE
and PROBABILITY

H. R. PITT
Ph.D., F.R.S.

Professor of Pure Mathematics
in the University of Nottingham

HAFNER PUBLISHING COMPANY

NEW YORK

Published in Great Britain by Oliver & Boyd Ltd.
Edinburgh and London, 1963

Printed in Great Britain by
Oliver & Boyd, Tweeddale Court, Edinburgh

TO MY FATHER AND SISTER

PREFACE

THE purpose of this book is to provide an introduction to the modern theory of probability and the mathematical ideas and techniques on which it is based. The fundamental ideas are those of measure and integration, and it is necessary to develop these in a sufficiently general context to make them applicable to a reasonably wide variety of spaces. The first part of the book is devoted to a treatment of these ideas from first principles and with the aim of providing working tools for use in the second part of the book. This aim is enough to determine within fairly close limits the scope of the treatment and I have made no attempt to include any topics that are not of immediate interest and relevance.

However, the demands of the theory of probability are substantial enough to ensure that this minimal treatment of measure and integration is also an adequate one in the sense that it includes most of the ideas and results needed for application in other branches of analysis.

The second part of the book presented much more difficult problems of selection. My aim has been to emphasise those points of the subject in which the underlying mathematical ideas, particularly those concerned with measure theory, appear to need the most care and attention. This part of the book is therefore obviously and inevitably incomplete, and it must be regarded as no more than an introduction to the much larger field of work covered by the major treatises (some of which are listed at the end) and the periodical literature.

No attempt has been made to include any account of applications to Statistics for the obvious reason that anything useful would have been far too long for a book of this size.

I am greatly indebted to Dr. D. Borwein for his help in reading the manuscript and for constructive criticisms and suggestions which led to the elimination of many errors and obscurities and to a substantial improvement in the treatment of some of the basic ideas in the first half of the book. The proofs were read by Dr. D. E. Rutherford, and I am particularly grateful to him for this and for his advice, encouragement and patience during the preparation of the book.

CONTENTS

Chapter 1

SETS AND SET-FUNCTIONS

§ 1. SET-OPERATIONS

The modern theories of measure and probability are based on fundamental notions of sets and set-functions which are now familiar and readily accessible. It is therefore simply on grounds of convenience that we begin with a brief summary of these ideas.

We shall be concerned with a space $\mathscr{X}$ of elements (points) x, subsets $X, X_1, X_2, \ldots$ of $\mathscr{X}$, and certain systems of subsets. In accordance with common usage, we write $x \in X$ to mean that the point x belongs to the set X and $X_1 \subset X_2$ to mean that the set X_1 is included in (or is a subset of) the set X_2. The empty set is denoted by 0, and it is plain that $X \subset X$ and $0 \subset X \subset \mathscr{X}$. Moreover, $X_1 \subset X_2$ and $X_2 \subset X_3$ together imply that $X_1 \subset X_3$, while $X_1 \subset X_2$ and $X_2 \subset X_1$ imply that $X_1 = X_2$.

The **operations** on sets are defined as follows. The set of points of $\mathscr{X}$ which are not in X is called the **complement** of X and written X'. It is clear that $(X')' = X$, $0' = \mathscr{X}$, $\mathscr{X}' = 0$ and, if $X_1 \subset X_2$, then $X_2' \subset X_1'$.

The **union** of any collection of sets is the set of points x which belong to at least one of them. The collection need not be finite or even countable. The union of two sets X_1, X_2 is written $X_1 \cup X_2$. The union of a finite or countable collection of sets X_n $(n = 1, 2, \ldots)$ is written $\bigcup_n X_n$. It is plain from the definition that the union operation does not depend on any particular ordering of the component sets and that there is no limit process involved even when the number of terms is infinite.

The **intersection** of a collection of sets is the set of points which belong to every set of the collection. The intersection of two sets is written $X_1 \cap X_2$, while the intersection of a sequence X_n is written $\bigcap_n X_n$. A pair of sets is **disjoint** if their intersection is 0 and a collection of sets is disjoint if every pair is disjoint. In particular, the union of a sequence

1

of sets X_1, X_2, ... can be expressed as the union of the disjoint sets X_1, $X_1' \cap X_2$, $X_1' \cap X_2' \cap X_3$, ...

The **difference** $X_1 - X_2 = X_1 \cap X_2'$ between the sets X_1 and X_2 is the set of points of X_1 which do not belong to X_2.

It is clear that each of the union and intersection operations is commutative and associative, while each is distributive with respect to the other in the sense that $X \cap (X_1 \cup X_2) = (X \cap X_1) \cup (X \cap X_2)$, $X \cup (X_1 \cap X_2) = (X \cup X_1) \cap (X \cup X_2)$ or, more generally, $X \cap (\bigcup X_v) = \bigcup (X \cap X_v)$, $X \cup (\bigcap X_v) = \bigcup (X \cap X_v)$. Furthermore, the operations are related to complementation by $X \cap X' = 0$, $X \cup X' = \mathcal{X}$, $(X_1 \cup X_2)' = X_1' \cap X_2'$, $(X_1 \cap X_2)' = X_1' \cup X_2'$ and, more generally,

$$(\bigcup X)' = \bigcap X', \quad (\bigcap X)' = \bigcup X'.$$

The sequence of sets X_n is **increasing** (and we write $X_n\uparrow$) if, for each n, $X_n \subset X_{n+1}$, and **decreasing** $(X_n\downarrow)$ if $X_{n+1} \subset X_n$. The upper limit, lim sup X_n, of a sequence is the set of points belonging to infinitely many of the sets; the lower limit, lim inf X_n, is the set of points belonging to X_n for all but a finite number of values of n. It follows that lim inf $X_n \subset$ lim sup X_n. If lim sup $X_n =$ lim inf $X_n = X$, X is called the **limit** of X_n and X_n is said to **converge** to X. We then write $X_n \to X$, or $X_n \uparrow X$, $X_n \downarrow X$ in the cases when X_n decreases or increases. It is plain from the definitions that lim inf $X_n = \bigcup_{n=1}^{\infty} \bigcap_{m=n}^{\infty} X_m$,

lim sup $X_n = \bigcap_{m=1}^{\infty} \bigcup_{n=m}^{\infty} X_n$. In particular, if X_n decreases, then

$$\bigcap_{m=n}^{\infty} X_m = \bigcap_{m=1}^{\infty} X_m, \quad \bigcup_{n=m}^{\infty} X_n = X_m,$$

$$\text{lim inf } X_n = \bigcap_{m=1}^{\infty} X_m = \text{lim sup } X_n,$$

$$\text{lim } X_n = \bigcap_{m=1}^{\infty} X_m.$$

Similarly, if X_n increases, lim $X_n = \bigcup_{n=1}^{\infty} X_n$.

§ 2. Additive Systems of Sets

A non-empty collection S of sets X in $\mathcal{X}$ is called a **ring** if, whenever X_1 and X_2 belong to S, so do $X_1 \cup X_2$ and $X_1 - X_2$. The empty set can be expressed as $0 = X - X$ and therefore belongs to every ring. Moreover, since $X_1 \cap X_2 = (X_1 \cup X_2) - \{(X_1 - X_2) \cup (X_2 - X_1)\}$, the intersection of two sets of S also belongs to S. The result of applying a finite number of union, intersection or difference operations to elements of a ring is therefore to give another element of the ring. In other words, the ring is **closed** under these operations.

The ring is also closed under the complement operation if (and only if) $\mathscr{X}$ itself belongs to the ring, but we do not assume that this is the case in general.

A ring S which contains $\mathscr{X}$ and has the further property that the union of any countably infinite collection of its members also belongs to S is called a σ-**ring**. Since

$$\bigcap X_n = (\bigcup X_n')',$$

it follows that a σ-ring also contains the intersection of any countable collection of its members and is thus closed under union, intersection, difference and complement operations repeated a finite or countably infinite number of times.

We shall often be concerned with the construction of a ring or σ-ring to include a given collection T of sets of X and the following theorem is fundamental.

THEOREM 1.   *A given collection T of subsets of space $\mathscr{X}$ is contained in a unique minimal ring (σ-ring) which is contained in every ring (σ-ring) which contains T.*

The minimal ring is called the ring **generated** by T. The minimal σ-ring generated by T is called the **Borel extension** of T, and its members are called **Borel sets**.

There is at least one ring containing T, namely the ring of all subsets of $\mathscr{X}$. We consider all such rings. It is plain that their intersection, consisting of the sets which belong to every such ring is itself a ring and has the properties stated, and the proof remains valid if we substitute σ-ring for ring throughout. In applications, T is usually a ring but not a σ-ring. The theorem still holds in a trivial sense if T is itself a σ-ring, but it is then its own Borel extension.

If $\mathscr{X}$ is the space $\mathscr{R}$ of real numbers, the intervals do not form a ring since the union of two intervals need not be an interval. However, the collection of sets which consist of a finite union of intervals of type $a \leq x < b$ do form a ring which is plainly the ring generated by these intervals in the sense of the last theorem. This ring does not contain $\mathscr{R}$ and is not a σ-ring. There is a straightforward generalisation to the space $\mathscr{R}_k$ of real vectors $(x_1, x_2, ..., x_k)$ in which a finite union of rectangles $a_j \leq x < b_j$ $(j = 1, 2, ..., k)$ is called a **figure** and the ring generated by the rectangles is the **ring of figures**.

The ring of figures, particularly in the case $n = 1$, is of fundamental importance in the theory of measure and integration. The ring is easy to visualise and provides useful concrete example on which the significance of abstract theorems may be illustrated.

§ 3. ADDITIVE SET FUNCTIONS

A set function $\mu(X)$ is a function whose range of definition is a system (usually a ring) of sets X and whose values belong to some appropriate space. We shall deal in this book only with set functions whose values are real numbers, but it is convenient to augment these by appending the elements $\pm \infty$ and giving them algebraic and order properties in relation to real numbers ξ according to the following scheme.

$$-\infty < \xi < \infty, \quad (\pm \infty) + (\pm \infty) = \xi + (\pm \infty) = \pm \infty;$$

$$\xi(\pm \infty) = (\pm \infty)\xi = \pm \infty \quad \text{or} \quad \mp \infty \quad \text{according as} \quad \xi > 0, \xi < 0.$$

$$(\pm \infty)(\pm \infty) = \infty, \quad (\pm \infty)(\mp \infty) = -\infty.$$

The operations $\infty - \infty$, ∞/∞, $0.\infty$ are not defined.

A set function $\mu(X)$ defined in a ring S is called **additive** if

$$\mu(\bigcup X_n) = \sum \mu(X_n)$$

for every *finite* disjoint collection of sets in S. The function is **completely additive** in S if the additivity property holds also for countably infinite collections of sets in S provided also that $\bigcup X_n$ belongs to S. This last proviso is not needed when S is a σ-ring since it is satisfied automatically. Otherwise, it must be retained and only certain sequences of sets (those whose union belongs to S) may be admitted.

We shall always assume that $\mu(X)$ is finite for at least one set X, so that $\mu(X) = \mu(X \cup 0) = \mu(X) + \mu(0)$ and $\mu(0) = 0$. It is not possible for an additive set function to take the value $+\infty$ on one set and $-\infty$ on another, since its value on their union would then be undefined; and we shall exclude this possibility by admitting $+\infty$ as a possible value, but not $-\infty$. A set function which takes neither of the values $\pm \infty$ is called **finite**.

A non-negative and completely additive function $\mu(X)$ defined over a σ-ring is called a **measure**. It is called a **probability measure** if $\mu(\mathscr{X}) = 1$.

A set function μ is said to be **continuous from below** at X if $\mu(X_n) \to \mu(X)$ whenever $X_n \uparrow X$. It is **continuous from above** at X if $\mu(X_n) \to \mu(X)$ whenever $X_n \downarrow X$ and $\mu(X_N) < \infty$ for some N. It is **continuous** at X if it is continuous from above and below at X unless $X = 0$, in which case continuity means continuity from above. The relationship between additivity and complete additivity is expressed in terms of continuity in the following theorem.

THEOREM 2. *A completely additive function μ is continuous. Conversely, an additive function is completely additive if it is continuous from below at every set or if it is finite and continuous at 0.*

(The ring in which the function is defined may, but need not, be a σ-ring.)

Suppose that μ is completely additive. If $X_n \uparrow X$ and $\mu(X_n) \neq \pm\infty$ for every n, we have

$$X = X_1 \cup \bigcup_{v=2}^{\infty} (X_v - X_{v-1}),$$

$$\mu(X) = \mu(X_1) + \sum_{v=2}^{\infty} \mu(X_v - X_{v-1})$$

$$= \mu(X_1) + \lim_{n \to \infty} \sum_{v=2}^{n} \mu(X_v - X_{v-1})$$

$$= \lim_{n \to \infty} \mu(X_n).$$

If $\mu(X_M) = \infty$, we have $\mu(X_n) = \mu(X_M) + \mu(X_n - X_M) = \infty$ and $\mu(X) = \mu(X_M) + \mu(X - X_M) = \infty$, since $\mu(X) \neq -\infty$ for any X. On the other hand, if $X_n \downarrow X$ and $\mu(X_N) < \infty$, we have

$$X_N = X \cup \bigcup_{v=N}^{\infty} (X_v - X_{v+1}),$$

$$\mu(X_N) = \mu(X) + \sum_{v=N}^{\infty} \mu(X_v - X_{v+1}) = \mu(X) + \lim_{n \to \infty} \sum_{v=N}^{n} \mu(X_v - X_{v+1})$$

$$= \mu(X) + \mu(X_N) - \lim_{n \to \infty} \mu(X_n).$$

Hence, μ is continuous.

To prove the converse, we suppose that Y_v are disjoint and

$$X = \bigcup_{v=1}^{\infty} Y_v, \quad X_n = \bigcup_{v=1}^{n} Y_v,$$

so that $X_n \uparrow X$. Then

$$\sum_{v=1}^{\infty} \mu(Y_v) = \lim_{n \to \infty} \sum_{v=1}^{n} \mu(Y_v) = \lim_{n \to \infty} \mu(X_n)$$

by finite additivity, and this is $\mu(X)$ if we assume that μ is continuous below at X. But we may also write

$$\mu(X) = \mu(X_n) + \mu(X - X_n) = \sum_{v=1}^{n} \mu(Y_v) + \mu(X - X_n)$$

by finite additivity, and this gives the same conclusion if μ is finite and continuous at 0.

The next theorem of Hahn and Jordan shows how a set function

B

taking positive and negative values can be expressed as the sum of positive and negative component set functions. This is of great practical importance, since it means that results about general set functions can be deduced almost immediately from those about measures.

THEOREM 3 (*Hahn-Jordan decomposition theorem*). *Suppose that* $\mu(X)$ *is completely additive in a σ-ring* S *of sets* X *in* $\mathscr{X}$, *let* M, m *be the upper and lower bounds of* $\mu(X)$ *in* S *and* $-\infty < m \leqq M \leqq \infty$. *Then* $\mathscr{X} = \mathscr{X}^+ \cup \mathscr{X}^-$, *where* $\mathscr{X}^+$ *and* $\mathscr{X}^-$ *belong to* S (*and either may be empty*) *and*

$$m = \mu(\mathscr{X}^-) \leqq \mu(X) \leqq 0 \quad \text{for} \quad X \subset \mathscr{X}^-, \tag{1}$$

$$0 \leqq \mu(X) \leqq \mu(\mathscr{X}^+) = M \quad \text{for} \quad X \subset \mathscr{X}^+. \tag{2}$$

Moreover, $\mu(X) = \mu^+(X) + \mu^-(X)$, *where* $\mu^+(X)$ *and* $\mu^-(X)$ *are uniquely defined and completely additive in* S *and*

$$\mu^+(X) = \mu(X \cap \mathscr{X}^+) = \sup_{Y \subset X} \mu(Y) \geqq 0,$$

$$\mu^-(X) = \mu(X \cap \mathscr{X}^-) = \inf_{Y \subset X} \mu(Y) \leqq 0.$$

COROLLARY 1. *If* $\mu(X) < \infty$ *for all* X, *then* $M < \infty$ *and* $\mu(X)$ *is bounded.*

COROLLARY 2. *If* $|\mu|(X) = \mu^+(X) - \mu^-(X)$, *then*

$$\sup_{Y \subset X} |\mu(Y)| \leqq |\mu|(X).$$

Let $\varepsilon_k > 0$, $\Sigma \varepsilon_k < \infty$. Then we can define sets A_k in S so that $m \leqq \mu(A_k) \leqq m + \varepsilon_k$ for $k = 1, 2, 3, \ldots$. Since

$$A_2 = (A_1 \cap A_2) \cup (A_2 - A_1), \quad (A_2 - A_1) \cup A_1 = A_1 \cup A_2,$$

we have

$$\mu(A_2) = \mu(A_1 \cap A_2) + \mu(A_2 - A_1), \quad \mu(A_2 - A_1) + \mu(A_1) = \mu(A_1 \cup A_2).$$

Further, $\quad m \leqq \mu(A_1 \cap A_2) = \mu(A_2) + \mu(A_1) - \mu(A_1 \cup A_2)$

$$\leqq m + \varepsilon_1 + m + \varepsilon_2 - m$$

$$= m + \varepsilon_1 + \varepsilon_2.$$

The same argument applied to the sets $A_n, A_{n+1}, \ldots A_p$ gives

$$m \leqq \mu \left\{ \bigcap_{v=n}^{p} A_v \right\} \leqq m + \sum_{v=n}^{p} \varepsilon_v,$$

and it follows from the continuity of μ that

$$m \leqq \mu \left\{ \bigcap_{v=n}^{\infty} A_v \right\} \leqq m + \sum_{v=n}^{\infty} \varepsilon_v.$$

If we now define $\mathscr{X}^- = \lim \inf A_k$, we have

$$\bigcap_{v=n}^{\infty} A_v \uparrow \mathscr{X}^- \text{ as } n \to \infty,$$

and it follows again from the continuity of μ that

$$\mu(\mathscr{X}^-) = \lim_{n \to \infty} \mu \left\{ \bigcap_{v=n}^{\infty} A_v \right\} = m.$$

If $X \subset \mathscr{X}^-$, then $\mathscr{X}^- = X \cup (\mathscr{X}^- - X),$

$$m = \mu(\mathscr{X}^-) = \mu(X) + \mu(\mathscr{X}^- - X) \geqq \mu(X) + m,$$

and so $\mu(X) \leqq 0$, which completes the proof of (1). On the other hand, if $X \subset \mathscr{X}^+ = \mathscr{X} - \mathscr{X}^-$, we have

$$m \leqq \mu(X \cup \mathscr{X}^-) = \mu(X) + \mu(\mathscr{X}^-) = \mu(X) + m, \quad \mu(X) \geqq 0.$$

We can now define sets B_n of S so that $\mu(B_n) \to M$, and since $B_n = (B_n \cap \mathscr{X}^-) \cup (B_n \cap \mathscr{X}^+)$, it follows that

$$\mu(\mathscr{X}^+) = \mu(B_n \cap \mathscr{X}^+) + \mu(\mathscr{X}^+ - B_n) \geqq \mu(B_n \cap \mathscr{X}^+)$$

$$\geqq \mu(B_n \cap \mathscr{X}^-) + \mu(B_n \cap \mathscr{X}^+) = \mu(B_n)$$

and $\mu(\mathscr{X}^+) = M$.

Finally, if $Y \subset X$,

$$\mu(Y) = \mu(Y \cap \mathscr{X}^+) + \mu(Y \cap \mathscr{X}^-) \leqq \mu(Y \cap \mathscr{X}^+)$$

$$\leqq \mu(Y \cap \mathscr{X}^+) + \mu\{(X - Y) \cap \mathscr{X}^+\} = \mu(X \cap \mathscr{X}^+)$$

and $\mu(Y) \geqq \mu(X \cap \mathscr{X}^-)$ similarly. The complete additivity of $\mu^+(X)$ and $\mu^-(X)$ is obvious.

§ 4. ADDITIVE FUNCTIONS ON RINGS OF FIGURES IN $\mathscr{R}_k$

We introduce here certain important set functions defined on the ring of figures described in Section 2. We begin with the case $k = 1$ and suppose that $\mu(x)$ is a non-decreasing and finite *point* function in $-\infty < x < \infty$. It is familiar that the left and right limits $\mu(x-0)$, $\mu(x+0)$ exist at every point x and that $\mu(x-0) \leqq \mu(x) \leqq \mu(x+0)$. We then define

$$\mu(I) = \Sigma\{\mu(b_v - 0) - \mu(a_v - 0)\} \tag{1}$$

when I is the figure formed by the union of the disjoint intervals $a_v \leqq x < b_v$. It is easy to verify that $\mu(I)$ is non-negative and *finitely* additive in the ring of figures I. In the important special case $\mu(x) = x$, $\mu(I)$ is simply the length of I.

The following result, that $\mu(I)$ is *completely* additive, is of fundamental importance in the theory of integration in $\mathscr{R}$.

THEOREM 4. *The set function $\mu(I)$ defined by* (1) *in respect to a non-decreasing point function $\mu(x)$ is completely additive in the ring of figures in $\mathcal{R}$.*

After Theorem 2, it is sufficient to show that if I_n are figures and $I_n\downarrow 0$, then $\mu(I_n)\to 0$. If not, we can define $d>0$ so that $\mu(I_n)>d$ for all n. But since $\mu(b-0) = \lim_{x\to b-0} \mu(x)$, we can construct a figure I_2^* and a *closed* figure J_2 so that

$$I_2^* \subset J_2 \subset I_1, \quad \mu(I_2^*)>d.$$

By repeating the process, we can construct sequences of figures I_n^* and *closed* figures J_n so that

$$I_n^* \subset J_n \subset I_{n-1}^* \subset I_{n-1}, \quad \mu(I_n^*)>d,$$

and the last inequality implies that I_n^* and, *a fortiori*, J_n are not empty. The sets J_n are therefore closed, decreasing and not empty and we appeal to the theorem that the intersection of such a sequence is not empty to deduce that J_n, and therefore I_n, have a common point. This is inconsistent with our assumption that $I_n\downarrow 0$, and it follows that $\mu(I_n)\to 0$.

If $\mu(x)$ is not necessarily monotonic, but $\Sigma\,|\,\mu(\beta_v)-\mu(\alpha_v)\,|$ is bounded for all finite sets of non-overlapping intervals (α_v, β_v) in an interval I $(a\leqq x<b)$, we say that $\mu(x)$ has **bounded variation**, in I, and the result of Theorem 4 can be extended easily to point functions of this kind. The function

$$\mu_1(x) = \sup \Sigma\{\mu(\beta_v)-\mu(\alpha_v)\},$$

where the summation is over all finite sets of intervals (α_v, β_v) in $a\leqq\alpha_v<\beta_v<x$, is plainly increasing and bounded in I, and it is easy to see that $\mu_2(x) = \mu_1(x)-\mu(x)$ has the same property. Thus we can express $\mu(x)$ as the difference $\mu_1(x)-\mu_2(x)$ of two bounded, increasing point functions. These define completely additive set functions $\mu_1(I)$, $\mu_2(I)$ over the ring of figures, by Theorem 4, and it follows that $\mu(I) = \mu_1(I)-\mu_2(I)$ is also completely additive and satisfies (1).

This shows that there is no gain in generality in considering any but non-negative functions $\mu(I)$ and we shall generally make this restriction throughout the book except in a few places where the contrary is stated.

If $\mu(x)$ is of bounded variation in every finite interval, it can still be expressed in the form $\mu_1(x)-\mu_2(x)$ in which $\mu_1(x)$, $\mu_2(x)$ will be increasing, but not necessarily bounded. They are bounded in $(-\infty, \infty)$ if and only if $\Sigma\,|\,\mu(\beta_v)-\mu(\alpha_v)\,|$ is bounded for all non-overlapping intervals (α_v, β_v) in $(-\infty, \infty)$, and $\mu(x)$ is then said to have bounded variation in $(-\infty, \infty)$.

This result can be generalised, with hardly more than verbal change in the proof, to rings of figures in $\mathscr{R}_k$ $(k > 1)$, but the close relationship between the set function on the ring and a point function over $\mathscr{R}_k$ is then not so important.   We shall not have occasion to use anything beyond the familiar case in which the set function extends the concept of area or volume.

The **volume** (**area** if $k = 2$) of the k-dimensional rectangle $a_j \leqq x_j < b_j$ is defined by $\prod\limits_{j=1}^{k} (b_j - a_j)$, and it is easy to verify that if a figure is decomposed into rectangles in different ways, the sum of volumes of its component rectangles is still the same.   This sum $\mu(I)$ for a figure I can therefore be called the **volume** of I without ambiguity, and the following theorem is a straightforward generalisation of the case $F(x) = x$ of Theorem 4.

THEOREM 5.   *The volume $\mu(I)$ of a figure I is completely additive in the ring of figures in $\mathscr{R}_k$.*

Chapter 2

GENERAL THEORY OF INTEGRATION
AND MEASURE

§ 5. Definition of an Integral

We suppose that the space $\mathscr{X}$ contains a ring of sets, called **simple sets**, on which a completely additive, finite-valued and non-negative set function $\mu(I)$ is defined, and that $\mathscr{X}$ is the limit of a sequence of simple sets. We call such a set function a **simple measure**. We then consider functions $f = f(x)$ defined on $\mathscr{X}$ and taking real † values (and possibly $\pm\infty$), and use the customary definitions

$$f^+ = f^+(x) = \sup [f(x), 0], \quad f^- = f^-(x) = \inf [f(x), 0], \quad (1)$$

so that

$$f = f^+ + f^-, \quad |f| = f^+ - f^-.$$

We write $f \geqq g$ if $f(x) \geqq g(x)$ for every x in $\mathscr{X}$, and $f_n \to f$ if $f_n(x) \to f(x)$ for every x in $\mathscr{X}$ as $n \to \infty$. We also need a general rule that the values of functions must be restricted, whenever necessary, to ensure the validity of any algebraic operations done on them. For example, $f \pm g$ cannot be defined if $f = \infty$, $g = \mp\infty$; fg cannot be defined if $f = \infty$, $g = 0$.

A function θ is called a **simple function** if it takes constant finite values a_j in each of a finite number of disjoint simple sets I_j and vanishes elsewhere, and we define

$$A(\theta) = \Sigma a_j \mu(I_j).$$

It is plain that if θ is simple, so are θ^+, θ^- and $|\theta|$ and that any finite linear combination $\Sigma a_v \theta_v$ of simple functions is also simple with

$$A(\Sigma a_v \theta_v) = \Sigma a_v A(\theta_v). \quad (2)$$

In particular,

$$A(\theta) = A(\theta^+) + A(\theta^-), \quad A(|\theta|) = A(\theta^+) - A(\theta^-).$$

† The theory can be extended to complex-valued functions by treating their real and imaginary parts separately and using Theorem 11 and the inequalities $|\alpha|, |\beta| \leq |\alpha + i\beta| \leq |\alpha| + |\beta|$ whenever necessary.

Finally,

$$A(\theta) \geqq 0 \qquad \text{if } \theta \geqq 0,$$

$$A(\theta_1) \geqq A(\theta_2) \quad \text{if } \theta_1 \geqq \theta_2.$$

For any function f (not generally simple), we define

$$L(f) = \inf \Sigma \, A(\theta_m)$$

for all sequences of simple functions θ_m which satisfy

$$\theta_m \geqq 0, \quad |f| \leqq \Sigma \theta_m.$$

Such a sequence always exists since we may define simple sets I_m so that $I_m \to \mathscr{X}$ and define $\theta_m = m$ in I_m, $\theta_m = 0$ in I'_m. We write $L(f) = \infty$ if $\Sigma A(\theta_m)$ diverges for every such sequence θ_n, but we note that $L(f)$ may be finite even if f takes infinite values at certain points. It is obvious that $L(|f|) = L(f)$, $L(af) = |a| L(f)$, $L(f^+) \leqq L(f)$, $L(f^-) \leqq L(f)$.

THEOREM 1. *If $|f| \leqq |g|$, then $L(f) \leqq L(g)$.*

If $\varepsilon > 0$, we can define simple functions $\theta_m \geqq 0$ so that $|f| \leqq |g| \leqq \Sigma \theta_m$, while $\Sigma A(\theta_m) \leqq L(g) + \varepsilon$. Then $L(f) \leqq \Sigma A(\theta_m) \leqq L(g) + \varepsilon$ for every positive ε and therefore $L(f) \leqq L(g)$.

THEOREM 2. *If Σf_n is defined for a finite or countable sequence of functions f_n, then $L(\Sigma f_n) \leqq \Sigma L(f_n)$.*

If $\varepsilon > 0$, we choose simple functions $\theta_{nm} \geqq 0$ so that

$$|f_n| \leqq \sum_m \theta_{nm}, \quad \sum_m A(\theta_{nm}) \leqq L(f_n) + 2^{-n} \varepsilon.$$

Then

$$\left| \sum f_n \right| \leqq \sum_n \sum_m \theta_{nm},$$

$$L\left(\sum f_n \right) \leqq \sum_n \sum_m A(\theta_{nm}) \leqq \sum_n \{ L(f_n) + 2^{-n} \varepsilon \} \leqq \sum_n L(f_n) + \varepsilon,$$

which is sufficient.

This last result for two functions f_1, f_2 shows that the functions f for which $L(f) < \infty$ form a linear metric space with $L(f)$ as metric.

THEOREM 3. *If $L(f_n) < \infty$ and $L(f - f_n) \to 0$, then $L(f)$, $L(f^+)$, $L(f^-)$ are finite and*

$$L(f^+ - f_n^+) \to 0, \quad L(f^- - f_n^-) \to 0, \quad L(|f| - |f_n|) \to 0,$$

$$L(f_n) \to L(f), \quad L(f_n^+) \to L(f^+), \quad L(f_n^-) \to L(f^-), \quad L(|f_n|) \to L(|f|).$$

The first part follows from the inequalities

$$L(f) = L(f_n + f - f_n) \leqq L(f_n) + L(f - f_n) < \infty,$$

by Theorem 2. The second part follows from Theorem 1 and the elementary inequalities

$$\left|f^{+}-f_{n}^{+}\right|\leqq\left|f-f_{n}\right|, \quad \left|f^{-}-f_{n}^{-}\right|\leqq\left|f-f_{n}\right|, \quad \left|\,|f|-|f_{n}|\,\right|\leqq\left|f-f_{n}\right|.$$

For the last part, we observe that

$$L(f)-L(f_{n}-f)\leqq L(f_{n})\leqq L(f)+L(f_{n}-f),$$

by Theorem 2.

THEOREM 4. *If θ_{n} is a sequence of simple functions and $\theta_{n}\downarrow 0$ for every x, then $A(\theta_{n})\rightarrow 0$.*

Let $C = \sup \theta_{1}(x)$ and let I_{1} be the (simple) set in which $\theta_{1}(x)>0$. Then if $\varepsilon>0$, the set I_{n} in which $\theta_{n}(x)\geqq\varepsilon$ is simple and $A(\theta_{n})\leqq C\mu(I_{n})$ $+\varepsilon\mu(I_{1})$. Since $I_{n}\downarrow 0$ and μ is completely additive, it follows from Theorem 2 of Chapter 1 that $\mu(I_{n})\rightarrow 0$ and so $\limsup A(\theta_{n})\leqq\varepsilon\mu(I_{1})$ for every $\varepsilon>0$, and therefore $A(\theta_{n})\rightarrow 0$.

THEOREM 5. *If θ is a simple function, then*

$$L(\theta) = A(|\,\theta\,|) = A(\theta^{+})-A(\theta^{-}) = L(\theta^{+})+L(\theta^{-}),$$

$$A(\theta) = A(\theta^{+})+A(\theta^{-}) = L(\theta^{+})-L(\theta^{-}).$$

In particular,

$$L(\theta^{+}) = A(\theta^{+}), \quad L(\theta^{-}) = -A(\theta^{-})$$

and, if $\theta\geqq 0$,

$$L(\theta) = A(\theta).$$

It is obviously enough to consider the case $\theta\geqq 0$. It follows from the trivial observation $\theta\leqq\theta$ that $L(\theta)\leqq A(\theta)$. Now suppose that $\theta\leqq\Sigma\theta_{m}$, $\theta_{m}\geqq 0$, and let $\eta_{M} = \theta- \sum_{m=1}^{M}\theta_{m}$. Then η_{M} is simple and decreases and $\lim \eta_{M}\leqq 0$ as $M\rightarrow\infty$. It follows that $\eta_{M}^{+}\downarrow 0$ and therefore, by Theorem 4, $A(\eta_{M}^{+})\rightarrow 0$. But

$$\theta = \sum_{m=1}^{M}\theta_{m}+\eta_{M}\leqq \sum_{m=1}^{M}\theta_{m}+\eta_{M}^{+},$$

$$A(\theta)\leqq \sum_{m=1}^{M}A(\theta_{m})+A(\eta_{M}^{+}),$$

and on letting $M\rightarrow\infty$, we have $A(\theta)\leqq\Sigma A(\theta_{m})$. Since this holds for all sequences θ_{m} with $\theta_{m}\geqq 0$, $\theta\leqq\Sigma\theta_{m}$, it follows that $A(\theta)\leqq L(\theta)$.

We say that f is **integrable** in $\mathscr{X}$ with respect to μ if we can define a sequence of simple functions θ_{n} so that $L(f-\theta_{n})\rightarrow 0$. If this is satisfied, it follows from Theorem 3 that $L(f), L(f^{+}), L(f^{-})$ are finite, and we write $\int f d\mu = L(f^{+})-L(f^{-})$ and call this expression the **integral** of f over $\mathscr{X}$ with respect to μ. A complex function is integrable if its real and imaginary parts are integrable.

§ 6. Properties of the Integral

THEOREM 6. *If f is integrable, so are f^+, f^- and $|f|$. Also*
$$\int f d\mu = L(f^+) - L(f^-) = \int f^+ d\mu + \int f^- d\mu,$$
$$\int |f| \, d\mu = L(f) = L(f^+) + L(f^-) = \int f^+ d\mu - \int f^- d\mu.$$

The first part follows at once from Theorem 3, with $f_n = \theta_n$, and the definition of the integral. In the second part, we have only to prove that $L(f) = L(f^+) + L(f^-)$ and this follows from Theorem 3 and the identity $L(\theta_n) = L(\theta_n^+) + L(\theta_n^-)$ of Theorem 5.

THEOREM 7. *A simple function θ is integrable and $\int \theta d\mu = A(\theta)$.*

This follows at once from the definition and Theorem 5.

THEOREM 8. *If θ_n is simple and $\theta_n \uparrow \lambda$, $L(\lambda) < \infty$, then $L(\lambda - \theta_n) \to 0$, λ is integrable and $\int \lambda d\mu = \lim \int \theta_n d\mu$.*

We note first that $\lim A(\theta_n)$ exists since $A(\theta_n)$ increases and is bounded by $L(\lambda)$. Then since $\theta_m - \theta_{m-1}$ is non-negative and simple and

$$\lambda - \theta_n = \sum_{m=n+1}^{\infty} (\theta_m - \theta_{m-1}),$$

we deduce from Theorems 2 and 5 that

$$L(\lambda - \theta_n) \leqq \sum_{m=n+1}^{\infty} A(\theta_m - \theta_{m-1}) = \sum_{m=n+1}^{\infty} \{A(\theta_m) - A(\theta_{m-1})\}$$
$$= \lim_{M \to \infty} A(\theta_M) - A(\theta_n),$$

and the first part follows. The second part comes from Theorems 3, 5 and 7.

COROLLARY. *If $L(f) < \infty$, we can define an integrable function λ so that $|f| \leqq \lambda$.*

THEOREM 9. *If f_n is integrable and $L(f - f_n) \to 0$, then f is integrable and*
$$\int f_n d\mu \to \int f d\mu, \quad \int f_n^+ d\mu \to \int f^+ d\mu, \quad \int f_n^- d\mu \to \int f^- d\mu, \quad \int |f_n| \, d\mu \to \int |f| \, d\mu.$$

By the definition of the integral, we can define simple functions θ_n so that $L(f_n - \theta_n) \to 0$. Then

$$L(f - \theta_n) = L(f - f_n + f_n - \theta_n) \leqq L(f - f_n) + L(f_n - \theta_n) = o(1),$$

and f is integrable. The second part follows then from Theorem 3 and the definition of the integral.

THEOREM 10. *If $L(f) = 0$, then f is integrable and*
$$\int f d\mu = \int |f| \, d\mu = 0.$$

We need only take $\theta_n = \theta$ in the definition. A function of this type is called a **nul-function**.

THEOREM 11. *If f is real and integrable,* $\left| \int f d\mu \right| \leq \int |f|\, d\mu$. *If f is complex and integrable, so is $|f|$ and the same inequality holds.*

If f is real,

$$\left| \int f d\mu \right| = \left| L(f^+) - L(f^-) \right| \leq L(f^+) + L(f^-) = \int |f|\, d\mu.$$

If f is complex and integrable, we can define complex valued simple functions θ_n so that $L\{|f - \theta_n|\} \to 0$, and the conclusion follows from the inequalities $L\{|f| - |\theta_n|\} \leq L\{|f - \theta_n|\}$ and $\left| A(\theta_n) \right| \leq A(|\theta_n|)$.

THEOREM 12. *A finite linear combination $\Sigma a_n f_n$ of integrable functions f_n is integrable (provided that it is defined for all x) and*

$$\int \{\Sigma a_n f_n\} d\mu = \Sigma a_n \int f_n d\mu$$

This follows at once from Theorem 9 and the linearity property (2) of Section 5 for the approximating simple function.

COROLLARY. *If f and g are integrable, so are $\sup(f, g) = f + (g - f)^+$ and $\inf(f, g) = f + (g - f)^-$.*

THEOREM 13. *If f and g are integrable and $g \leq f$, then $\int g d\mu \leq \int f d\mu$. In particular, $\int f d\mu \geq 0$ if $f \geq 0$.*

The special case is obvious from the definition, and the general inequality follows from Theorem 12, since

$$\int f d\mu = \int \{g + (f - g)\} d\mu = \int g d\mu + \int (f - g) d\mu$$

and $f - g \geq 0$. As an immediate corollary, we have

THEOREM 14 (*Mean-value Theorem*). *If f is integrable and if $c \leq f \leq C$ in a simple set I and $f = 0$ outside I, then $c\mu(I) \leq \int f d\mu \leq C\mu(I)$.*

THEOREM 15. *If $\{f_n\}$ is a finite set of integrable functions, and Σf_n is defined for all x, then $\left| \int \Sigma f_n d\mu \right| \leq \Sigma \int |f_n|\, d\mu$.*

For $\left| \int \Sigma f_n d\mu \right| \leq \int |\Sigma f_n|\, d\mu \leq \int \Sigma |f_n|\, d\mu = \Sigma \int |f_n|\, d\mu$ by Theorems 11, 13, and 12.

The theorems above show that the integrable functions form a linear space L which is also a metric space with $L(f)$ as metric. We shall write $f \in L$ (or $f \in L_\mu$ when the specification is necessary) to mean that f is integrable.

We define f_X for a function f and a set X to be the function which is equal to f in X and vanishes outside. If γ is the unit function taking the value 1 at every point of $\mathscr{X}$, γ_X is called the **characteristic function** of the set X and takes the values 1 or 0 according as x is in X or X'. A set X is called a **nul set** or a **set of zero measure** if γ_X is a nul function, so that $L(\gamma_X) = \int \gamma_X d\mu = 0$. Any subset of a nul set is obviously a nul set. A property which holds outside a nul set is said to hold **almost everywhere** (abbreviated to a.e.). In particular, we shall write $f \geqq g$ a.e. if $f(x) \geqq g(x)$ for almost all x, and $f_n \to f$ a.e. if $f_n(x) \to f(x)$ for almost all x in $\mathscr{X}$.

THEOREM 16. *The sum of a sequence of nul functions is a nul function provided that the sum is defined for all x. The union of a sequence of nul sets is a nul set.*

The first part follows immediately from Theorem 2, and it is sufficient to prove the second part in the case when the nul sets X_n are disjoint and have union X. Then $\gamma_X = \Sigma \gamma_{X_n}$, and the conclusion follows from the first part.

THEOREM 17. (i) *If f is integrable, then $|f| < \infty$ a.e.* (ii) *If f is nul, then $f = 0$ a.e.* (iii) *Conversely, if $f = 0$ a.e., then f is nul.* (iv) *An integrable function remains integrable and has the same integral after its values (including $\pm \infty$) are changed in a nul set.*

If $c > 0$, let γ_c be the characteristic function of the set in which $|f| \geqq c$, so that γ_∞ denotes the characteristic function of the set in which $f(x) = \pm \infty$. Then since $\gamma_\infty \leqq \gamma_c \leqq |f|/c$ for $0 < c < \infty$, we have $L(\gamma_\infty) \leqq L(\gamma_c) \leqq c^{-1} L(f)$, and on letting $c \to \infty$, we get $L(\gamma_\infty) = 0$, which gives (i). But if f is nul, $L(f) = 0$, and the last inequality gives $L(\gamma_c) = 0$ for $c > 0$. The set in which $f \neq 0$ is the union of the sets γ_c with $c = 1, \frac{1}{2}, \frac{1}{3}, \ldots$, and is therefore nul by Theorem 16.

It is sufficient to prove (iii) in the case when $|f| = \infty$ in a nul set X and $f = 0$ in X'. Then if we define functions $\lambda_m = \gamma_X$ for $m = 1$, 2, 3, $\ldots$, we have $L(\lambda_m) = 0$, and since $\lambda_m = \gamma_X = 1$ in X, it follows that $|f| = \infty = \lambda = \Sigma \lambda_m$ in X, while $|f| = 0 \leqq \lambda$ in X'. Hence, $|f| \leqq \lambda$, $L(f) \leqq L(\lambda) \leqq \Sigma L(\lambda_m) = 0$.

For (iv), suppose that $f = g$ outside a nul set. Let $f_1 = f$, $g_1 = g$ when $f = g$ and f and g are both finite, and let $f_1 = g_1 = 0$ in the remaining nul set. Then $f_1 = g_1$, $f = f_1 + (f - f_1)$, $g = g_1 + (g - g_1)$ for all x, and it follows from Theorem 12 and (i) and (iii) above that $\int f d\mu = \int g d\mu$.

An important consequence of this theorem is that we can ignore the values of a function or sequence of functions in any nul set. In fact, the functions need not be defined in a nul set, and the preceding theorems, particularly Theorems 12, 13, 14 and 15, can be generalised in this sense.

THEOREM 18 (*Convergence Theorem*). *Suppose that $f_n \in L$ for $n = 1, 2, \ldots, |f_n| \leqq \lambda, \lambda \in L$, and that $f_n \to f$ a.e. Then $f \in L$ and*
$$\int f_n d\mu \to \int f d\mu, \quad \int |f_n - f| \, d\mu \to 0.$$

Moreover, the theorem remains valid if n is replaced by a continuous real variable t in an interval $-\infty \leq a < t < b \leq \infty$ *and the limit is taken as* $t \to a$ *or* $t \to b$.

We first prove as lemmas two special cases of the theorem.

LEMMA 1. *If* ξ_n *is simple,* $\xi_n \geq \xi_{n+1} \geq 0$ *and* $\xi_n \to 0$ *a.e., then* $\int \xi_n d\mu \to 0$.

We can write $\xi_1 - \xi_n \uparrow \beta$, where β is defined for all x since ξ_n is monotonic. Since $\xi_1 - \xi_n$ is simple and β, the sum of ξ_1 and a nul function, is integrable, it follows from Theorems 8 and 12 that

$$\int \xi_1 d\mu - \int \xi_n d\mu = \int (\xi_1 - \xi_n) d\mu \to \int \beta d\mu = \int \xi_1 d\mu,$$

and the conclusion follows.

LEMMA 2. *Suppose that, for each n,* λ_n *is the limit of an increasing sequence of non negative simple functions, that* $L(\lambda_1) < \infty$, λ_n *decreases for all x and* $\lambda_n \to 0$ *a.e. Then* $L(\lambda_n) \to 0$.

Let $\varepsilon > 0$, $\varepsilon_m > 0$, $\Sigma \varepsilon_m = \varepsilon$. By Theorem 8, we can define simple functions η_m so that $L(\lambda_m - \eta_m) < \varepsilon_m$, $0 \leq \eta_m \leq \lambda_m$. Then $\xi_n = \inf_{m \leq n} \eta_m$ is simple, ξ_n decreases and since $0 \leq \xi_n \leq \eta_n \leq \lambda_n$, it follows that $\xi_n \downarrow 0$ a.e. and therefore, by Lemma 1, $L(\xi_n) = \int \xi_n d\mu \to 0$. But λ_m decreases and

$$\lambda_n = \inf_{m \leq n} \lambda_m = \inf_{m \leq n} \{\eta_m + (\lambda_m - \eta_m)\} \leq \xi_n + \sum_{m=1}^{n} (\lambda_m - \eta_m),$$

$$L(\lambda_n) \leq L(\xi_n) + \sum_{m=1}^{n} L(\lambda_m - \eta_m) \leq \varepsilon + o(1),$$

and the conclusion follows.

Proof of Theorem 18. If $\varepsilon > 0$, $\varepsilon_v > 0$, $\Sigma \varepsilon_v = \varepsilon$, we define simple functions θ_v so that
$$L(f_v - \theta_v) \leq \varepsilon_v.$$
Then

$$\sup_{v \geq n} |f_v - \theta_v| \leq \sum_{v=n}^{\infty} |f_v - \theta_v|,$$

$$L\left\{\sup_{v \geq n} |f_v - \theta_v|\right\} \leq \sum_{v=n}^{\infty} L(f_v - \theta_v) \leq \sum_{v=n}^{\infty} \varepsilon_v = o(1)$$

as $n \to \infty$. But

$$\lim \sup |f_v - \theta_v| \leq \sup_{v \geq n} |f_v - \theta_v|$$

for all n, and it follows that $\lim \sup |f_v - \theta_v|$ is a nul function and vanishes a.e. Since $f_v \to f$ a.e., it then follows that $\theta_v \to f$ a.e. and, by the general principle of convergence, that

$$\lambda_n = \sup_{i, j \geq n} |\theta_i - \theta_j| \to 0 \quad \text{a.e.}$$

Moreover, λ_n obviously decreases for every x,

$$\lambda_1 \leqq 2 \sup \left| \theta_v \right| \leqq 2 \sup \left| f_v \right| + 2 \sup \left| f_v - \theta_v \right| \leqq 2\lambda + 2 \Sigma \left| f_v - \theta_v \right|,$$

$L(\lambda_1) \leqq 2L(\lambda) + \varepsilon < \infty$, and λ_n therefore satisfies the conditions of Lemma 2, and $L(\lambda_n) \to 0$. But since

$$\left| f - \theta_n \right| = \lim_{i \to \infty} \left| \theta_i - \theta_n \right| \leqq \lambda_n \quad \text{a.e.,}$$

it follows that $L(f - \theta_n) \to 0$. This shows that $f \in L$ and the conclusion follows from this and (2) and Theorems 2 and 3.

The analogous form for the continuous variable t follows immediately since $\int f_t d\mu \to \int f d\mu$ and $\int \left| f_t - f \right| d\mu \to 0$ as $t \to b$ through any sequence of values and this is true only if the limits exist as $t \to b$ through all values.

The following theorem for series follows as an immediate corollary of Theorem 18.

THEOREM 19. *Suppose that* $a_n \in L$ *for* $n = 1, 2, \ldots,$

$$\left| \sum_{v=1}^{n} a_v \right| \leqq \lambda, \quad \lambda \in L.$$

and that $\displaystyle\sum_{v=1}^{\infty} a_v = s$ *a.e. Then s is integrable and*

$$\int s d\mu = \sum_{v=1}^{\infty} \int a_v d\mu.$$

The following convergence theorem, though weaker than Theorem 18, is often useful.

THEOREM 20. *Suppose that* $f_n \in L$ *for* $n = 1, 2, \ldots,$ *and* $f_n \uparrow f$ *a.e. Then*

$$\lim_{n \to \infty} \int f_n d\mu = \int f d\mu$$

in the sense that if one side exists, so does the other, and the two are equal. Moreover, the theorem remains valid if n is replaced by a continuous variable as in Theorem 18.

The existence of the right-hand side means that $f \in L$ and therefore $\left| f_n \right| \leqq \sup \left\{ \left| f_1 \right|, \left| f \right| \right\}$ and the conclusion follows from Theorem 18.
Conversely, if the left hand side is finite,

$$L(f) = L\left\{ f_1 + \sum_{v=2}^{\infty} (f_v - f_{v-1}) \right\} \leqq L(f_1) + \sum_{v=2}^{\infty} L(f_v - f_{v-1})$$

$$= L(f_1) + \lim_{n \to \infty} \sum_{v=2}^{n} \left\{ \int f_v d\mu - \int f_{v-1} d\mu \right\}$$

$$= L(f_1) - \int f_1 d\mu + \lim_{n \to \infty} \int f_n d\mu < \infty,$$

by Theorems 2 and 12, and the conclusion follows from Theorem 18 and the corollary of Theorem 8.

§ 7. MEASURABILITY AND MEASURE

A function is **measurable** if it is the limit a.e. of a sequence of simple functions.

A simple function is obviously measurable and so is the unit function γ, since it is the limit of characteristic functions of a sequence of simple sets whose limit is $\mathscr{X}$. The following theorems show how measurability is preserved under the familiar analytic operations.

THEOREM 21. *The modulus and positive and negative components of a measurable function are measurable. If two functions f and g are measurable, so are $f \pm g$, fg, sup (f, g), inf (f, g), f/g, provided that they are defined a.e.*

All these results except the last follow immediately from the fact that the operations applied to simple functions produce simple functions. In the last part, we can suppose that $f = 1$ and define simple functions θ_n so that $\theta_n \to g$ a.e. We then define simple sets I_n so that $I_n \to \mathscr{X}$ and define the simple functions ξ_n by

$$\xi_n = \theta_n^{-1} \text{ when } \theta_n \neq 0, \quad \xi_n = 1 \text{ when } \theta_n = 0, \; x \in I_n,$$

$$\xi_n = 0 \text{ when } \theta_n = 0, \; x \in I'_n.$$

It is plain that ξ_n is simple and $\xi_n \to g^{-1}$ a.e.

THEOREM 22. *In order that f be integrable it is necessary and sufficient that it be measurable and $L(f) < \infty$.*

Necessity is clear from the first part of the proof of Theorem 18 (with $f_v = f$). Conversely, we suppose that θ_n is simple, $\theta_n \to f$ a.e. and (using the corollary of Theorem 8) that $|f| \leq \lambda$, $\lambda \in L$. If we let $\lambda_n = \theta_n$ if $|\theta_n| \leq \lambda$, $\lambda_n = \lambda$ if $\theta_n > \lambda$, $\lambda_n = -\lambda$ if $\theta_n < -\lambda$, it follows that $|\lambda_n| \leq \lambda$ and λ_n is integrable by the corollary of Theorem 12. Since $\lambda_n \to f$ a.e., the conclusion follows from Theorem 18.

THEOREM 23. *If f_n is measurable for $n = 1, 2, 3, \ldots$, so are lim sup f_n and lim inf f_n. In particular, if $f_n \to f$ a.e., then f is measurable.*

We prove the theorem first in the special case $f_n \to f$ a.e. We can subdivide $\mathscr{X}$ into a sequence of disjoint simple sets I_j with $0 < \mu(I_j) < \infty$ and the function h defined to be equal to $[j^2 \mu(I_j)]^{-1}$ in I_j is positive and integrable by Theorem 20.

Since f_n is measurable, we can define simple functions θ_{nv}, each vanishing outside a finite union of sets I_j, so that $\lim\limits_{v\to\infty} \theta_{nv} = f_n$ a.e. for each n. Then

$$g_{nv} = \frac{h\theta_{nv}}{h + |\theta_{nv}|} \to g_n \quad \text{a.e.,}$$

where

$$g_n = \frac{hf_n}{h + |f_n|} \text{ if } f_n \neq \pm\infty, \quad g_n = \pm h \text{ if } f_n = \pm\infty,$$

and g_n is measurable since g_{nv} is simple. Also $g_n \to g$ a.e. where

$$g = \frac{hf}{h + |f|} \text{ if } f \neq \pm\infty, \quad g = \pm h \text{ if } f = \pm\infty.$$

But $|g_n| \leq h$ and h is integrable and it therefore follows from Theorems 18 and 22 that g is measurable, and we can define simple functions θ_n, each vanishing outside a finite union of sets I_j, so that $|\theta_n| < h$, $\theta_n \to g$ a.e. Then $\theta_n h[h - \theta_n]^{-1}$ is simple and tends almost everywhere to f, and it follows that f is also measurable.

In the general case, it follows from Theorem 21 and what we have just proved that

$$\sup_{v \geq n} f_v = \lim_{m\to\infty} \sup_{m \geq v \geq n} f_v$$

is measurable, and so also

$$\lim \sup f_n = \lim_{n\to\infty} \sup_{v \geq n} f_v.$$

We can treat $\lim \inf f_n$ similarly.

A set X is **measurable** if its characteristic function γ_X is measurable.

Any simple set is measurable and so is $\mathscr{X}$. If X is measurable and $L(\gamma_X) < \infty$, then γ_X is integrable by Theorem 22 and we define the **measure** $\mu(X)$ of X by $\mu(X) = \int \gamma_X d\mu$. If X is measurable and $L(\gamma_X) = \infty$, we say that X has infinite measure and write $\mu(X) = \infty$.

The notation $\mu(X)$ is consistent with that of the original simple measure $\mu(I)$ on the simple sets, so that we may think of $\mu(X)$ as an extension of the simple measure to a wider system of sets. In particular, a nul set is simply a measurable set of zero measure.

If $f \in L$ and X is measurable, $f\gamma_X$ is integrable by Theorems 21 and 22 and its integral is called the **integral of f over X** and written

$$F(X) = \int_X f d\mu.$$

The essential properties of measurable sets and integrals over them can be summarised as follows.

THEOREM 24. (i) *The measurable sets form a σ-ring on which $\mu(X)$ is a measure and an extension of the simple measure $\mu(I)$; and $\mu(\mathscr{X}) < \infty$ if and only if $\mu(I)$ is bounded on simple sets.* (ii) *If $f \in L$, then*

$$F(X) = \int_X f d\mu, \quad F^+(X) = \int_X f^+ d\mu, \quad F^-(X) = \int_X f^- d\mu$$

are completely additive on the σ-ring of measurable sets. (iii) *$F^+(X)$, $F^-(X)$ are the Hahn-Jordan components of $F(X)$ in the sense of Chapter 1, and if $F(X) = 0$ for all measurable X, then f is nul.*

If $f \geqq 0$ is measurable and X, X_1, X_2 are measurable sets, $f_X = f\gamma_X$ is measurable by Theorem 21 and

$$f_{X'} = f - f_X, \quad f_{X_1 \cup X_2} = \sup [f_{X_1}, f_{X_2}].$$

If X_1, X_2, ... are measurable and disjoint, and $X = \bigcup X_v$, then $f_X = \Sigma f_{X_v}$. In particular, we may substitute $f = \gamma$ and the first part of (i) follows at once from the definitions and Theorems 21, 22 and 23. The second part comes from the fact that $I_n \to \mathscr{X}$ and so $\mu(I_n) \to \mu(\mathscr{X})$ for some sequence of simple sets I_n. If f is integrable, (ii) follows for f^+ from Theorems 12 and 18, and the conclusions extend at once to f^- and f.

For (iii) we need only observe that $F^+(X)$ and $F^-(X)$ have the properties of the Hahn-Jordan components and that this decomposition is unique by Theorem 3 of Chapter 1. Finally, if $F(X) = 0$ for all measurable X, it follows that $F^+(\mathscr{X}) = F^-(\mathscr{X}) = 0$ and therefore f^+, f^- and f are all nul.

The Borel extension of the simple sets depends only on the sets and not on any measure defined in them. Since it is the minimal extension, it is contained in the σ-ring of measurable sets defined by any simple measure $\mu(I)$, and every Borel set is measurable. The converse is not generally true, although the following theorems show that a measurable set is almost a Borel set in a certain sense. We say that f is a **Borel function** if † $\mathscr{E}\{f > c\}$ is a Borel set for every real c.

THEOREM 25. (i) *In order that f be measurable it is necessary and sufficient that $\mathscr{E}\{f > c\}$ be measurable for every real c.* (ii) *A Borel function is measurable and every measurable function is equal a.e. to a Borel function.* (iii) *A measurable set differs from a Borel set by a nul set.*

First suppose that $\mathscr{E}\{f > c\}$ is measurable for every c. Then

---

† In the usual notation, $\mathscr{E}\{\ \ \}$ is the set in which the property specified inside the brackets holds.

$X_\infty = \mathscr{E}\{f = \infty\} = \bigcap_{v=1}^{\infty} \mathscr{E}\{f > v\}$ and $X_{-\infty} = \mathscr{E}\{f = -\infty\}$ are measurable and

$$X_{nv} = \mathscr{E}\left\{\frac{v+1}{n} \geq f > \frac{v}{n}\right\} = \mathscr{E}\left\{f > \frac{v}{n}\right\} n \, \mathscr{E}'\left\{f > \frac{v+1}{n}\right\}$$

is measurable for $n = 1, 2, 3, \ldots, v = 0, \pm 1, \pm 2, \ldots$, and so are the characteristic functions $\gamma_\infty, \gamma_{-\infty}, \gamma_{nv}$ of $X_\infty, X_{-\infty}, X_{nv}$. The function

$$g_n = \frac{1}{n} \sum_{v=-\infty}^{\infty} v\gamma_{nv} + n\gamma_\infty - n\gamma_{-\infty}$$

is also measurable and $g_n \to f$ a.e., and this proves the sufficiency part of (i) and the first part of (ii).

Conversely, if f is measurable, we define simple functions θ_n so that $\theta_n \to f$ a.e. Then if $f_1 = \liminf \theta_n$,

$$\mathscr{E}\{f_1 > c\} = \bigcup_v \mathscr{E}\{\theta_n \geq c + 1/v \text{ except for a finite set of } n\}$$

$$= \bigcup_v \liminf_{n \to \infty} \mathscr{E}\{\theta_n \geq c + 1/v\}$$

is obtained by countable set operations on the simple sets $\mathscr{E}\{\theta_n \geq c + 1/v\}$ and is therefore a Borel set. Hence f_1 is a Borel function and $f - f_1$ is nul since $\theta_n \to f$ a.e. This establishes the second part of (ii), and (iii) follows from this and the fact that $X = \mathscr{E}\{\gamma_X > \frac{1}{2}\}$.

THEOREM 26. *The measurable sets derived from a simple measure* $\mu(I)$ *form the minimal σ-ring which contains the simple sets and all nul sets; and $\mu(X)$ is the only possible extension of $\mu(I)$ to this σ-ring.*

We shall call $\mu(X)$ **the Lebesgue extension of** $\mu(I)$.

COROLLARY. *If the simple measure is itself defined over a σ-ring, its Lebesgue extension is the measure obtained by adding the nul sets (if any) which are not already included as simple sets. Moreover, the integral derived from a simple measure μ is identical with that obtained by replacing μ by its Lebesgue extension and treating the latter as a simple measure.*

The first part follows at once from Theorem 25 (iii). For the second part, we note that in the proof of Theorem 25 with $f = \gamma_X$, the measure of $\mathscr{E}\{\theta_n \geq \frac{1}{2} + 1/v\}$ is defined uniquely by the simple measure and the same is true, by the continuity of μ, for $\mathscr{E}\{f_1 > \frac{1}{2}\}$. This differs by a nul set from X and it is therefore sufficient to show that if μ^* is any other measure extension of $\mu(I)$, then $\mu^*(X) = 0$ when $\mu(X) = 0$. This follows from the fact that if $\mu(X) = 0$, $\varepsilon > 0$, we can define simple sets I_j so that $X \subset \bigcup I_j$, $\Sigma\mu(I_j) < \varepsilon$, and then $\mu^*(\bigcup I_j) \leq \Sigma\mu^*(I_j) = \Sigma\mu(I_j) < \varepsilon$.

c

A completely additive set function $F(X)$ defined on a σ-ring is called **absolutely continuous** with respect to a measure $\mu(X)$ on the same σ-ring if $F(X) \to 0$ uniformly as $\mu(X) \to 0$. In other words, if $\varepsilon > 0$, we can define $\delta(\varepsilon) > 0$ so that $|F(X)| < \varepsilon$ for all measurable sets X with $\mu(X) < \delta$.

In fact, when $\mu(X)$ is derived from a simple measure, it is enough to have this condition for simple sets. For if X is measurable and we suppose that $F(X)$ is non-negative and $\mu(X) \leq \frac{1}{4}\delta$, we can use Theorem 8 and the definition of L to define simple functions θ_n so that $\theta_n \uparrow \lambda$, $\gamma_X \leq \lambda$, $\int \lambda d\mu \leq \frac{1}{2}\delta$; and it follows that the simple sets $I_n = \mathscr{E}\{\theta_n > \frac{1}{2}\}$ increase to a limit J which contains X. By the definition of I_n, $\frac{1}{2}\mu(I_n) \leq \int \theta_n d\mu \leq \int \lambda d\mu \leq \frac{1}{2}\delta$, and then $F(I_n) \leq \varepsilon$ and by the complete additivity of $F(X)$, $F(X) \leq F(J) = \lim F(I_n) \leq \varepsilon$.

THEOREM 27.   *If $f \in L$, then $F(X) = \int_X f d\mu$ is absolutely continuous.*

If $\varepsilon > 0$, we define a simple function θ so that $\int |f - \theta| \, d\mu < \frac{1}{2}\varepsilon$. Then if $C = \sup |\theta|$ and X is measurable,

$$|F(X)| \leq \int_X |f| \, d\mu \leq \int_X |\theta| \, d\mu + \int_X |f - \theta| \, d\mu \leq C\mu(X) + \tfrac{1}{2}\varepsilon \leq \varepsilon$$

for $\mu(X) \leq \varepsilon/2C$.

We have proved in Theorems 24 and 27 that the integral $F(X)$ of an integrable function is absolutely continuous and completely additive. The next theorem gives a converse to this and also gives some information about the structure of more general set functions which are not necessarily absolutely continuous.

THEOREM 28 (*Radon-Nikodym Theorem*).   *Suppose that $H(X)$ is completely additive in the σ-ring of sets measurable with respect to a measure $\mu(X)$ in $\mathscr{X}$. Then there is a unique decomposition*

$$H(X) = F(X) + Q(X)$$

in which $Q(X)$ satisfies

$$Q(X) = Q(X \cap S)$$

for some fixed nul set S, $F(X)$ is absolutely continuous and

$$F(X) = \int_X f d\mu$$

for some function f (unique except for a nul function) which is integrable over every X for which $H(X)$ is finite.

In particular, if $H(X)$ itself is absolutely continuous, $Q(X) = 0$ and

$$H(X) = F(X) = \int_X f d\mu.$$

$Q(X)$ is called **singular component** of $H(X)$ and f is called the **Radon-Nikodym derivative** of $F(X)$.

Since we have assumed in our definition of simple sets that X is a countable union of simple sets of finite measure, it is enough to prove the theorem when $\mu(X) < \infty$, and after the Hahn-Jordan theorem, we may suppose that $H(X) \geq 0$.

We define T to be the class of integrable functions $t \geq 0$ for which

$$T(X) = \int_X t d\mu \leq H(X)$$

for all measurable X. We then define a sequence t_n in T so that

$$T_n(\mathscr{X}) \to T^* = \sup_{t \varepsilon T} T(\mathscr{X}) \leq H(\mathscr{X}) < \infty. \qquad (1)$$

If we now define

$$p_n = \sup_{v \leq n} t_v, \quad X_v = \mathscr{E}\{t_v = p_n, \ t_j < p_n \text{ for } j = 1, 2, ..., v-1\},$$

it follows that X_v are disjoint and measurable (by Theorem 25) and $X = \bigcup X_v$,

$$P_n(X) = \int_X p_n d\mu = \sum_{v=1}^{n} P_n(X_v) \leq \sum_{v=1}^{n} H(X_v) = H(X),$$

and therefore $p_n \in T$. But p_n increases and has a limit f which is also in T, by Theorem 20, and therefore

$$F(X) \leq H(X), \quad Q(X) = H(X) - F(X) \geq 0$$

for every measurable X. Also, since $T_n(\mathscr{X}) \leq P_n(\mathscr{X}) \leq T^*$, it follows from (1) that $P_n(\mathscr{X}) \to T^*$ and from Theorem 20 that $P_n(\mathscr{X}) \to F(\mathscr{X})$ and so

$$F(\mathscr{X}) = T^*. \qquad (2)$$

Now let

$$Q_n(X) = Q(X) - \mu(X)/n,$$

and let $\mathscr{X}_n^+$ and $\mathscr{X}_n^-$ be the sets defined for $Q_n(X)$ by the Hahn-Jordan theorem, so that

$$Q(X) \geq \mu(X)/n \text{ for } X \subset \mathscr{X}_n^+, \quad Q(X) \leq \mu(X)/n \text{ for } X \subset \mathscr{X}_n^-.$$

Then

$$H(X) \geq F(X) + \frac{\mu(X)}{n} = \int_X \left(f + \frac{1}{n}\right) d\mu \text{ for } X \subset \mathscr{X}_n^+$$

and this shows that the function equal to f in $\mathscr{X}_n^-$ and to $f+1/n$ in $\mathscr{X}_n^+$ belongs to T and therefore, after (2),

$$\frac{1}{n}\,\mu(\mathscr{X}_n^+)+F(\mathscr{X}) = \int_{\mathscr{X}_n^+}\left(f+\frac{1}{n}\right)d\mu+\int_{\mathscr{X}_n^-} fd\mu \le T^* = F(\mathscr{X}).$$

This implies that $\mu(\mathscr{X}_n^+) = 0$ for each n, and $S = \bigcup_n \mathscr{X}_n^+$ is nul. Since $X-S \subset \mathscr{X}_n^-$ for every n, it follows that $Q(X-S) = 0$ and $Q(X) = Q(X \cap S)+Q(X-S) = Q(X \cap S)$.

To prove uniqueness of $F(X)$ and $Q(X)$, we suppose that the decomposition can be done in two ways and

$$H(X) = F_1(X)+Q_1(X) = F_2(X)+Q_2(X),$$

where $F_1(X)$, $F_2(X)$ are integrals and $Q_1(X)$, $Q_2(X)$ vanish on all sets disjoint from the nul sets S_1, S_2 whose union S is also nul. Then

$$F_1(X) = F_1(X-X \cap S), \qquad F_2(X) = F_2(X-X \cap S),$$

$$F_1(X)-F_2(X) = Q_2(X-X \cap S)-Q_1(X-X \cap S) = 0.$$

The uniqueness of f, and therefore of $F(X)$ and $Q(X)$, follows from Theorem 24 (iii).

Finally, if $H(X)$ is absolutely continuous, so is $Q(X) = H(X)-F(X)$ by Theorem 27, and since an absolutely continuous function plainly vanishes on a nul set, $Q(X) = Q(X \cap S) = 0$.

If $G(X)$ is a completely additive set function over a σ-ring of sets X and if X is the countable union of sets X_v for which $G(X_v)$ is finite, we can decompose G into the two measures G^+ and $-G^-$ defined by the Hahn-Jordan Theorem of Chapter 1 and establish an integral with respect of each of them, using the whole σ-ring on which $G(X)$ is defined as the ring of simple sets. We then say that a function f is **integrable with respect to** G if it is integrable with respect to G^+ and $-G^-$, and we define the **integrals** $\int fdG$, $\int f\,|\,dG\,|$ by

$$\int fdG = \int fdG^+ - \int fd(-G^-), \quad \int f\,|\,dG\,| = \int fdG^+ + \int fd(-G^-).$$

The σ-ring of measurable sets will be the original σ-ring with the addition of nul sets if they are not already included. Since the two integrals on the right can be treated separately, there is no need for anything more than the theory already established and all the theorems proved for μ-measures can be applied immediately. The following extension of Theorem 11 is perhaps worth stating separately.

THEOREM 29. *If f is real or complex and integrable with respect to G, then* $\left|\int fdG\right| \le \int |f|\,|\,dG\,|$.

For

$$\left| \int f dG \right| = \left| \int f dG^+ - \int f d(-G^-) \right|$$
$$\leq \left| \int f dG^+ \right| + \left| \int f d(-G^-) \right|$$
$$\leq \int |f| \, dG^+ + \int |f| \, d(-G^-) \quad \text{(by Theorem 11)}$$
$$= \int |f| \, |dG|.$$

The following theorem shows that integrals with respect to G may be reduced to integrals with respect to another measure μ when G is absolutely continuous with respect to μ.

THEOREM 30.　*Suppose that $g \in L$, $G(X) = \int_X g d\mu$ and that f is measurable. Then $\int f dG = \int f g d\mu$ in the sense that if one integral exists, so does the other, and the two are equal.*

It is sufficient, in view of the decomposition $f = f^+ + f^-$, $G = G^+ + G^-$, where $G^+(X) = \int_X g^+ d\mu$, $G^-(X) = \int_X g^- d\mu$, by Theorem 24 (ii), to prove the result when $f \geq 0$, $g \geq 0$ and define simple sets I_n so that $I_n \uparrow \mathscr{X}$ and functions f_n by

$$f_n = \sup \, [f, n] \text{ in } I_n, \quad f_n = 0 \text{ in } I_n'.$$

Then since f is measurable, we can define a sequence of simple function θ_{nv} so that

$$0 \leq \theta_{nv} \leq n \text{ in } I_n, \quad \theta_{nv} = 0 \text{ in } I_n', \quad \theta_{nv} \to f_n \quad \text{a.e.}$$

It follows then from Theorem 18 and the fact that the present theorem is obviously true when f is replaced by a simple function that

$$\int f_n dG = \lim_{v \to \infty} \int \theta_{nv} dG = \lim_{v \to \infty} \int \theta_{nv} g d\mu = \int f_n g d\mu.$$

Since $f_n \uparrow f$, the conclusion follows from Theorem 20.

　　We end this section by showing how a mapping of a measure space $\mathscr{X}$ on to another space $\mathscr{Y}$ can be used to induce a measure and integral on the latter. We denote the mapping by $y = \alpha(x)$ and suppose that it maps the whole of $\mathscr{X}$ on to the whole of $\mathscr{Y}$ without assuming that it is necessarily one to one.

　　If Y is any set in $\mathscr{Y}$, its **inverse image** $\alpha^{-1}(Y)$ is the set of all points in $\mathscr{X}$ for which $\alpha(x) \in Y$. Then it is obvious that $Y_1, Y_2, \ldots$, are disjoint if and only if their inverse images are disjoint, and that

$$\alpha^{-1}\{\textstyle\bigcup_v Y_v\} = \textstyle\bigcup_v \alpha^{-1}(Y_v), \quad \alpha^{-1}\{\textstyle\bigcap_v Y_v\} = \textstyle\bigcap_v \alpha^{-1}(Y_v)$$

for finite or countable systems of sets Y_v, whether disjoint or not. It follows that the sets Y whose inverse images belong to a σ-ring in $\mathscr{X}$

form a σ-ring in $\mathscr{Y}$ and that the one to one correspondence between Y and $\alpha^{-1}(Y)$ determines an isomorphism between the two σ-rings in respect to set operations. In particular, if we have a measure μ in $\mathscr{X}$, the sets Y whose inverse images in $\mathscr{X}$ are μ-measurable form a σ-ring in $\mathscr{Y}$, and if we define $v(Y) = \mu\{\alpha^{-1}(Y)\}$ whenever $\alpha^{-1}(Y)$ is μ-measurable, it is easy to verify that $v(Y)$ is a measure in $\mathscr{Y}$. We call it the **measure induced** in $\mathscr{Y}$ by μ and α. We can then proceed to derive the integral in $\mathscr{Y}$ induced by μ and α by treating the induced measurable sets in $\mathscr{Y}$ as simple sets, and the relationship between integration in $\mathscr{X}$ and $\mathscr{Y}$ is shown in the following theorem.

THEOREM 31. *Suppose that $\mu(X)$ is a measure in $\mathscr{X}$ and $v(Y)$ the measure induced in $\mathscr{Y}$ by a mapping $y = \alpha(x)$ of $\mathscr{X}$ on to $\mathscr{Y}$. Then*

$$\int_{\mathscr{Y}} f(y)dv = \int_{\mathscr{X}} f[\alpha(x)]d\mu,$$

in the sense that if one integral exists, so does the other, and the two are equal.

After the Corollary of Theorem 26, the measurable sets in $\mathscr{X}$ may be taken as the simple sets through which the integral in $\mathscr{X}$ is defined.

The integral in $\mathscr{Y}$ is obtained by defining a **simple function** $\theta(y)$ in $\mathscr{Y}$ as one which takes constant values a_j in disjoint sets Y_j whose inverse images $X_j = \alpha^{-1}(Y_j)$ are measurable in $\mathscr{X}$, and $\theta(y)$ then defines uniquely the simple function $\theta[\alpha(x)]$ in $\mathscr{X}$. If A_v, L_v, A_μ, L_μ are defined in the two spaces as in Section 5, it follows that

$$A_v(\theta) = \Sigma a_j v(Y_j) = \Sigma a_j \mu[\alpha^{-1}(Y_j)] = \Sigma a_j \mu(X_j) = A_\mu[\theta[\alpha(x)]],$$

$$L_v(f) = L_\mu\{f[\alpha(x)]\}.$$

If $\int f(y)dv$ exists, and we express the condition for this in terms of simple functions and consider the associated simple function in $\mathscr{X}$, it follows at once that $\int f[\alpha(x)]d\mu$ exists and has the same value.

In proving the converse, we have to remember that the measurable sets, or even the simple sets, in $\mathscr{X}$ may not all be inverse images of sets in $\mathscr{Y}$ and it is therefore not enough to consider approximation to $\int f[\alpha(x)]d\mu$ by the most general kind of simple function in $\mathscr{X}$. In fact, this difficulty can be overcome by noting that

$$\mathscr{E}\{f[\alpha(x)]>c\} = \alpha^{-1}[\mathscr{E}\{f(y)>c\}]$$

for any real c, and the function $f[\alpha(c)]$ is therefore measurable and integrable with respect to the measure μ on the restricted σ-ring of measurable sets in $\mathscr{X}$ which are also inverse images of sets in $\mathscr{Y}$. The correspondence between simple functions can be used again and the conclusion follows.

It is important to notice that the measure induced in $\mathscr{Y}$ by the procedure described here may bear no relation to intrinsic properties of $\mathscr{Y}$ and may, in fact, not be a useful measure. What is needed in practice is an induced measure which includes among its measurable sets all those sets in $\mathscr{Y}$ which arise naturally. For example, if $\mathscr{Y}$ is $\mathscr{R}$, it would be most desirable that all Borel sets should be measurable and this can be ensured quite simply by demanding that the function $y = \alpha(x)$ should be measurable with respect to the measure μ in $\mathscr{X}$.

As an example of the theory, suppose that $\mathscr{X} = \mathscr{Y} = \mathscr{R}_k$, that the mapping of $\mathscr{X}$ on $\mathscr{Y}$ is defined by the non-singular matrix transformation $y = Cx$, and that μ in $\mathscr{X}$ is the classical Lebesgue extension of the volume of figures which is treated in detail in Chapter 3.

Then every figure in $\mathscr{Y}$ has an inverse image in $\mathscr{X}$ which is a parallelepiped and therefore μ-measurable, and ν is therefore defined for every Lebesgue measurable set in $\mathscr{Y}$. Moreover, it is easy to see by elementary co-ordinate geometry that ν is absolutely continuous with respect to the Lebesgue measure m in $\mathscr{Y}$ and has constant Radon-Nikodym derivative equal to $|C|^{-1}$, the ratio between the volumes of corresponding parallelepipeds in $\mathscr{X}$ and $\mathscr{Y}$ under the transformation. The conclusion of Theorem 31 then can be written

$$\int_{\mathscr{R}_k} f(y)dm = |C| \int_{\mathscr{R}_k} f[Cx]dm.$$

In more general cases, particularly when the mapping is not one to one, it is essential to bear in mind that the class of functions $f[\alpha(x)]$ which can appear as integrands in the integral $\int f[\alpha(x)]d\mu$ is restricted by the nature of $\alpha(x)$. For example, if $\mathscr{X} = \mathscr{Y} = \mathscr{R}$ and $\alpha(x) = \sin x$, $f[\alpha(x)]$ is necessarily periodic in $-\infty < x < \infty$. No difficulty arises in any application of the theorem if we start by thinking of $f(y)$ as given over $\mathscr{Y}$. Thus, the extension of the last formula to the case in which $y = \alpha(x)$ is a general differentiable one to one mapping of a set $\mathscr{X}$ of $\mathscr{R}_k$ on to a set $\mathscr{Y}$ of $\mathscr{R}_k$, takes the form

$$\int_{\mathscr{R}_k} f(y)dm = \int_{\mathscr{R}_k} f[\alpha(x)]J(x)dm,$$

where $J(x)$ is the Jacobian of $\alpha(x)$. The proof requires more intricate elementary analysis, but no new idea.

§ 8. PRODUCT MEASURES AND MULTIPLE INTEGRALS

If $\mathscr{X}$ and $\mathscr{Y}$ are two spaces of points x and y, the space of ordered pairs (x, y) is called their **Cartesian product space** and written $\mathscr{X} \otimes \mathscr{Y}$. The following theorem shows how **a product measure** and integration can be extended to a product space when they have been established in the spaces separately.

THEOREM 32. *Suppose that $\mu(I)$, $v(J)$ are simple measures in rings of (simple) sets I, J in $\mathscr{X}$ and $\mathscr{Y}$. Then the* **simple sets** K in $\mathscr{X} \otimes \mathscr{Y}$, *each consisting of finite union of* **rectangular sets** *of type $I \otimes J$, form a ring on which there is a simple measure $m(K)$ such that $m(K) = \mu(I)v(J)$ when $K = I \otimes J$.*

We define $m(K)$ for a simple set to be the sum of $\mu(I)v(J)$ for its component rectangular sets $I \otimes J$. There is no ambiguity in this as it is easy to verify that the sum is unchanged if the decomposition into rectangular sets is carried out in a different way. It is also easy to see that the simple sets form a ring on which $m(K)$ is *finitely* additive.

All that remains is to show that $m(K) = \sum_{v=1}^{\infty} m(K_v)$ if $K_v = I_v \otimes J_v$ and K are rectangular sets, $K = \bigcup K_v$, and K_v are disjoint.

Let $\gamma = \gamma(x, y)$, $\gamma_v = \gamma_v(x, y)$ be the characteristic functions of K, K_v, respectively, so that $\gamma = \sum_{v=1}^{\infty} \gamma_v$. For each v, γ_v is integrable in $\mathscr{Y}$ for each fixed x and

$$\int \gamma_v dv = v(J_v) \text{ for } x \text{ in } I_v,$$

$$\int \gamma_v dv = 0 \quad \text{for } x \text{ outside } I_v.$$

Hence, $\int \gamma_v dv$ is integrable with respect to μ and

$$\int d\mu \int \gamma_v dv = \mu(I_v)v(J_v) = m(K_v).$$

But it follows from Theorem 19 that $\gamma = \Sigma \gamma_v$ is also integrable with respect to v and that

$$\int \gamma dv = \int \Sigma \gamma_v dv = \Sigma \int \gamma_v dv.$$

By Theorem 19 again, this is integrable with respect to μ and $m(K) = \int d\mu \int \gamma dv = \int d\mu \, \Sigma \int \gamma_v dv = \Sigma \int d\mu \int \gamma_v dv = \Sigma \, m(K_v)$.

The function $m(K)$ can now be used to establish a measure $m(W)$ over a σ-ring of measurable sets in $\mathscr{X} \otimes \mathscr{Y}$ and an associated space of integrable functions. Their integrals over $\mathscr{X} \otimes \mathscr{Y}$ are generally called **multiple integrals** to distinguish them from the **repeated integrals** already used in the proof of the last theorem. In fact, the two kinds of integrals are closely related as the following theorem shows.

THEOREM 33 (*Fubini*). *If μ and v are measures in $\mathscr{X}$ and $\mathscr{Y}$ and if* $f = f(x, y)$ *is measurable with respect to the product measure m of μ and v, it is measurable with respect to μ and v for almost all y and x, respectively, and the existence of any one of the integrals*

$$\int |f|\, dm, \quad \int d\mu \int |f|\, dv \quad \text{or} \quad \int dv \int |f|\, d\mu$$

implies the existence and equality of the integrals

$$\int f dm, \quad \int d\mu \int f dv, \quad \int dv \int f d\mu.$$

We may suppose that $f \geqq 0$ and that $f \leqq C$ in a simple set K and $f = 0$ in K'. The conclusion in general then follows from Theorem 20 by the argument used in Theorem 30. We can now define simple functions θ_v so that

$$0 \leqq \theta_v \leqq C, \quad \theta_v \to f \text{ in } K - S, \quad m(S) = 0.$$

If $\varepsilon > 0$, we can now define rectangular sets in K whose characteristic functions γ_v satisfy

$$\gamma_s \leqq \Sigma \gamma_j, \quad \Sigma \int \gamma_j dm < \varepsilon.$$

Then

$$L_\mu(L_v \gamma_s) \leqq \Sigma L_\mu(L_v \gamma_j) = \Sigma \int \gamma_j dm < \varepsilon$$

for every positive ε, and therefore for almost all x, γ_s is nul in y and $\theta_v \to f$ for almost all y. If we observe that the theorem is obviously true when f is a simple function, the conclusion in general follows from Theorem 18.

Chapter 3

INTEGRALS OF FUNCTIONS OF REAL VARIABLES

§ 9. LEBESGUE AND STIELTJES INTEGRALS

The general theory developed in Chapter 2 can be applied immediately to the case in which $\mathscr{X}$ is the k-dimensional space $\mathscr{R}_k$ of real vectors $(x_1, x_2, ..., x_k)$ and $\mu(I)$ is defined in the ring of figures defined in Section 4. We are concerned almost entirely in this chapter with the case $k = 1$, $\mathscr{X} = \mathscr{R}$ and the simple sets are then based on intervals $a \leqq x < b$ and the simple functions are called step functions and take constant values in intervals of this type. We have already seen that a simple measure can be obtained from an increasing point function $\mu(x)$, and we assume throughout the chapter that the measure $\mu(X)$ is obtained from such a simple measure by the methods described in Chapter 2. If $\mu(x)$ is not monotonic, but of bounded variation, it still defines a completely additive set function $\mu(X)$ and we can define the integral of a function f with respect to μ as in Section 7, so that

$$\int f d\mu = \int f d\mu^+ - \int f d(-\mu^-),$$

where $\mu^+(X)$, $\mu^-(X)$ are the components of $\mu(X)$ corresponding to two monotonic point functions. There is obviously no real restriction in confining the general theory to the monotonic case with $\mu(X) \geqq 0$, $\mu(x)$ increasing.

The integral $\int f d\mu$ of f with respect to a general increasing μ is called the **Lebesgue-Stieltjes integral** of f with respect to μ. In the particularly important case $\mu(x) = x$, the integral is called the **Lebesgue integral** of f (or simply the **integral** of f) and written $\int f dx$. The integrals can be defined over any set X which is measurable with respect to μ and when there is any possibility of having to deal with more than one measure, it is convenient to make sure of the necessary measurability conditions by supposing that f is a Borel function and X a Borel set. We show in Theorems 1, 2 and 3 below that there is little loss of generality in this.

We use the familiar notation $\int_a^b f dx$ for the integral of f over the interval with end points a and b, and note that it is immaterial whether the end points belong to the interval or not, since the measure of each of them is zero with respect to x. In the Stieltjes case, however, rather more care is needed, since a single point has positive measure with respect to $\mu(X)$ if it is a discontinuity of $\mu(x)$. When this occurs, we distinguish between the four possible cases by writing

$$\int_{a-0}^{b-0}, \quad \int_{a-0}^{b+0}, \quad \int_{a+0}^{b-0}, \quad \int_{a+0}^{b+0}$$

according as the interval is $a \le x < b$, $a \le x \le b$, $a < x < b$, $a < x \le b$, but there is no need for this complication if $\mu(x)$ is known to be continuous at a and b, since the four integrals are then all equal.

Since we are interested in this chapter in integrals over the very special space $\mathscr{R}$, it is important to see just how the specific properties of this space are involved in the theory. We have used the topological properties of $\mathscr{R}$ to establish the simple measures $\mu(X)$ over intervals, but when this has been done there is no need to refer to $\mathscr{R}$ throughout the whole of the theory developed in Chapter 2. We return to $\mathscr{R}$ only when we wish to investigate and characterise more closely the classes of measurable sets and integrable functions. Above all, we need to show that the theory applies to the sets and functions which arise naturally in analysis and which are generally classified by their algebraic and topological properties in relation to $\mathscr{R}$. The following theorems show that this can be done very satisfactorily.

THEOREM 1.   *Open and closed sets are Borel sets and therefore measurable with respect to every μ measure.*

Let X be open and let r be any rational point in X. Let $I(r)$ be the largest interval $r \le x < q$ contained in X. Then if ξ is any point of X, there is an interval $\xi - \delta < x < \xi + \delta$ contained in X, and we can choose a rational r in $\xi - \delta < r < x$ so that $I(r)$ contains x. Since the number of rationals in X is countable, this means that X is the countable union of intervals $I(r)$, and is therefore a Borel set. A closed set, being the complement of an open set, is therefore also a Borel set.

THEOREM 2.   *A monotonic function $f(x)$ is a Borel function.*

If $f(x)$ increases, the set $\mathscr{E}\{f(x) > c\}$ is an interval of one of the types $a < x < \infty$ or $a \le x < \infty$. The first is open and a Borel set by

Theorem 1. The second is the union of the open interval $a < x < \infty$ and the closed set consisting of the single point a.

THEOREM 3. *A continuous function $f(x)$ is a Borel function.*

If $X = \mathscr{E}\{f > c\}$ and $\xi \in X$, we can define $\delta > 0$, by the continuity of f at ξ, so that $f(x) > c$ for $\xi - \delta < x < \xi + \delta$ and the whole of this interval belongs to X. This means that X is open for every real c, and the conclusion follows from Theorem 1.

All that need be said now is that the functions of analysis are almost invariably derived from monotonic or continuous functions by algebraic or limit processes which leave intact their Borel properties.

§ 10. SOME THEOREMS OF THE INTEGRAL CALCULUS

Many theorems which are familiar and important in the Riemann Integral Calculus follow immediately for Lebesgue integrals from the results of Chapter 2, and there is no need to state them separately. There are other results, however, which are as familiar as these but which depend essentially on the specific properties of the space $\mathscr{R}$. We prove these theorems for Lebesgue integrals in this section and find that there is little extra trouble in dealing with the general Stieltjes form. The minor difficulties which this generalisation causes are due mainly to awkwardness in notation and can be minimised if we remember that μ in the integral $\int f d\mu$ represents a measure and not (in this context) a point function. This measure is defined by the function $\mu(x - 0)$ and is independent of the values of $\mu(x)$ at its points of discontinuity. On the other hand, the values of f at its discontinuities may very well affect the value of the integral and have to be treated with care. In formulæ involving repeated integrals or other complicated expressions, it is often advantageous to write $\int d\mu \, Q$ instead of $\int Q \, d\mu$, as we have already done in Section 8. This notation emphasises the fact that $\int$ and μ are the inseparable components of the symbol for the single operation of integration with respect to μ.

THEOREM 4 (*Change of variable*). *If $\alpha(t)$ is strictly increasing and continuous for $A \leq t \leq B$ and $\alpha(A) = a$, $\alpha(B) = b$, and if $G(x)$ is of bounded variation in $a \leq x \leq b$, then*

$$\int_{a-0}^{b+0} f(x) dG(x) = \int_{A-0}^{B+0} f[\alpha(t)] dG[\alpha(t)].$$

In particular,

$$\int_{a}^{b} f(x) dx = \int_{A}^{B} f[\alpha(t)] d\alpha(t)$$

and, if $\alpha(t) = \int_A^t \alpha'(u)du$, $\alpha'(u) \in L$, *then*

$$\int_a^b f(x)dx = \int_A^B f[\alpha(t)]\alpha'(t)dt.$$

These conclusions follow at once from Theorems 31 and 30 of Chapter 2. We show in Theorem 9 below that the condition in the last part is satisfied provided only that $\alpha(t)$ is absolutely continuous in the sense that its associated set function satisfies the condition in the definition preceding Theorem 27 of Section 7.

THEOREM 5 (*Integration by parts*). *Suppose that* $F(x)$, $G(x)$ *are of bounded variation over an interval containing a Borel set* X. *Then*

$$\int_X F(x-0)dG + \int_X G(x+0)dF = FG(X),$$

where FG *is the set function derived from the function* $F(x)G(x)$.

If the values of $F(x)$ *and* $G(x)$ *are normalised at common points of discontinuity so that*

$$F(x) = \tfrac{1}{2}[F(x+0)+F(x-0)], \quad G(x) = \tfrac{1}{2}[G(x+0)+G(x-0)],$$

then

$$\int_X F(x)dG + \int_X G(x)dF = FG(X).$$

In particular, if $F(x) = \int_a^x f(t)dt$, $G(x) = \int_a^x g(t)dt$, *then*

$$\int_a^b F(x)g(x)dx + \int_a^b f(x)G(x)dx = \left[F(x)G(x)\right]_a^b.$$

The three set functions are measures, or sums of at most four measures which are defined uniquely (Theorem 26 of Section 7) by their values for intervals, and it is therefore sufficient to prove the theorem in the case when X is the interval I: $a \leq x < b$.

The characteristic function of the set $a \leq x < b$, $a \leq x_1 \leq x$ in the product space (x, x_1) is integrable and the two repeated integrals of it with respect to $F(x)$ and $G(x_1)$ are equal, by Fubini's theorem. This gives

$$\int_I [G(x+0)-G(a-0)]dF(x) = \int_I [F(b-0)-F(x_1-0)]dG(x_1)$$

and on replacing x_1 by x, this becomes

$$\int_I F(x-0)dG + \int_I G(x-0)dF$$

$$= F(b-0)[G(b-0)-G(a-0)]+G(a-0)[F(b-0)-F(a-0)]$$

$$= F(b-0)G(b-0)-F(a-0)G(a-0)$$

$$= FG(I).$$

The second part follows at once if we interchange F and G and add. The last part follows from Theorem 30 of Section 7.

THEOREM 6 (*First mean value theorem*). *If f is integrable with respect to μ and $c \leq f \leq C$ in the interval J: $a \leq x \leq b$, then*

$$c\mu(J) \leq \int_J f d\mu \leq C\mu(J),$$

and if $f(x)$ is continuous in $a \leq x \leq b$, then $\int_J f d\mu = f(\xi)\mu(J)$ for some value of ξ in $a \leq \xi \leq b$.

The first part is a special case of Theorem 14 of Section 6 when J is replaced by a simple interval $a \leq x < b + 1/n$, and the conclusion follows from the complete additivity of $\mu(X)$ and $\int_X f d\mu$ as $n \to \infty$. The second part follows from the fact that a continuous function in a closed interval attains every value between its upper and lower bounds.

THEOREM 7 (*Second mean-value theorem*).

(i) *If f is integrable and ϕ monotonic in $a \leq x \leq b$, then*

$$\int_a^b f\phi \, dx = \phi(a) \int_a^\xi f \, dx + \phi(b) \int_\xi^b f \, dx$$

for some ξ in $a \leq \xi \leq b$.

(ii) *If ϕ decreases and $\phi \geq 0$, then*

$$\int_a^b f\phi \, dx = \phi(a) \int_a^\xi f \, dx$$

for some ξ in $a \leq \xi \leq b$.

We suppose that ϕ decreases and define $f(x) = 0$ outside $a \leq x \leq b$, $\phi(a-0) = \phi(a)$, $\phi(b+0) = \phi(b)$ and note that a similar proof applies if ϕ increases. Then if $F(x) = \int_a^x f(t)dt$, it follows from Theorem 5 applied to the interval $a \leq x \leq b$ and Theorem 30 of Section 7 that

$$\int_a^b f\phi \, dx = \mathop{\vphantom{\int}}_{a-0}^{\,b+0}\!\left[F\phi \right] - \int_{a-0}^{b+0} F \, d\phi$$

$$= \phi(b) \int_a^b f \, dt - [\phi(a) - \phi(b)] F(\xi)$$

for some ξ in $a \leq \xi \leq b$, by Theorem 6. This gives (i), and we deduce (ii) immediately by redefining $\phi(b) = 0$, since this change at one point does not change the first two terms in (i).

THEOREM 8 (*Differentiation under the integral sign*). *Suppose that* $f(x, t)$ *is integrable with respect to* x *in a neighbourhood of* t, *that* $\left| f(x, t+h) - f(x, t) \right| \leq \left| h \right| \lambda(x)$, $\lambda \in L$, *and that* $\dfrac{\partial f}{\partial t}$ *exists a.e. Then* $\dfrac{\partial f}{\partial t} \in L$ *and*

$$\int \frac{\partial f}{\partial t} \, dx = \frac{d}{dt} \int f(x, t) dt.$$

This follows from the continuous parameter case of Theorem 18 of Section 6.

The theory of integration described in Chapter 2 does not depend in any way on the notion of differentiation. In fact, there may not be any natural and simple way of defining the derivative of a set function $F(X)$ unless more is known about the topological properties of the space $\mathscr{X}$. The space $\mathscr{R}$, however, has a very rich and familiar topology and a fully developed theory of differentiation, and the close relationship between integration and differentiation is brought out by the fundamental theorem of calculus, that $F(x) = \int_a^x f(t) \, dt$ is differentiable at every continuity point of the Riemann integrable function f. The following theorem is equally fundamental in the Lebesgue theory and, together with the Radon-Nikodym theorem, shows how integration and differentiation can be treated as inverse operations.

THEOREM 9 (*Fundamental theorem of calculus*).

(i) *If* $f \in L(a, b)$, *then*

$$\lim_{h \to 0} \frac{1}{h} \int_0^h \left| f(x+t) - f(x) \right| dt = 0 \quad a.e. \text{ in } (a, b)$$

and $F(x) = \int_a^x f \, dt$ *is differentiable and* $F'(x) = f(x)$ *a.e. in* (a, b).

(ii) *If* $F(x)$ *is absolutely continuous, it is differentiable a.e.*, $F'(x)$ *is integrable, and* $F(x) = \int_a^x F'(t) dt$.

We make the trivial simplification that $a = 0$, $b = 1$ and suppose that $g \geq 0$, $g \in L(0, 1)$ $G(x) = \int_a^x g \, dt$. We then define the value of the step function $G_n(x)$ in each binary interval $v2^{-n} \leq x < (v+1)2^{-n}$ $(n \geq 1, v \geq 0)$ to be $2^n \int_{v2^{-n}}^{(v+1)2^{-n}} g \, dt$.

The **upper derivative** $D^+ G$ of G is defined in the usual way by

$$D^+ G(x) = \lim_{h \to 0} \sup [G(x+h) - G(x)]/h = \lim_{h \to 0} \sup \frac{1}{h} \int_0^h g(x+t) dt.$$

If $c>0$, the set E_n in which $g_n(x)\geq c$ is the union of binary intervals of length 2^{-n}; and if $2^{-n-1}< |h| \leq 2^{-n}$,

$$\frac{1}{h}\int_0^h g(x+t)dt \leq \frac{1}{2^n h}[g_n(x)+g_n(x-2^{-n})+g_n(x+2^{-n})]\leq 6c \tag{1}$$

unless x or $x\pm 2^{-n}$ belongs to E_n, when x must belong to the set E_n^* consisting of the intervals of E_n together with the adjoining intervals of length 2^{-n}. It follows that the set in which $h^{-1}\int_0^h g(x+t)dt > 6c$ for some value of h in $2^{-N-1}<h\leq 2^{-1}$ is contained in $\bigcup_{n=1}^N E_n^*$. This set can be obtained from $\bigcup_{n=1}^N E_n$ by replacing each disjoint interval of the latter by an interval three times as long (or less when there is overlapping), and therefore

$$\mu\left(\bigcup_{n=1}^N E_n^*\right) \leq 3\mu\left(\bigcup_{n=1}^N E_n\right), \tag{2}$$

where μ denotes Lebesgue measure.

Since $\bigcup_{n=1}^N E_n$ can be expressed as the union of disjoint intervals in each of which the mean value of $g(t)$ is at least c, it follows that

$$c\mu\left(\bigcup_{n=1}^N E_n\right) \leq \int_a^b g\,dt$$

and since this holds for all N, it follows that

$$c\mu\mathscr{E}\{D^+G>6c\}\leq 3\int_a^b g\,dt. \tag{3}$$

Now let $\varepsilon>0$ and define a step function $\theta(t)$ so that

$$\int_a^b g\,dt<\varepsilon. \quad g=|f-\theta|. \tag{4}$$

Then

$$\frac{1}{h}\int_0^h |f(x+t)-f(x)|\,dt$$

$$\leq \frac{1}{h}\int_0^h g(x+t)dt+g(x)+\frac{1}{h}\int_0^h |\theta(x+t)-\theta(x)|\,dt$$

and since the last term tends to 0 with h unless x is one of the finite number of discontinuities of $\theta(t)$, we get

$$\limsup_{h\to 0}\frac{1}{h}\int_0^h |f(x+t)-f(x)|\,dt\leq D^+G+g\leq 7c, \tag{5}$$

by (3) and (4), except in a set of measure at most $4\varepsilon/c$, since, $D^+G \leqq 6c$ except in a set of measure at most $3\varepsilon/c$, and $g(x) \leqq c$ except in a set of measure at most ε/c. Since ε may be arbitrarily small, it follows that (5) holds a.e., and since this is true for every positive c, we have the first part of (i). The second part then follows from the inequality

$$\left| \int_0^h f(x+t)dt - hf(x) \right| \leqq \int_0^h |f(x+h) - f(x)| \, dt,$$

and (ii) is a corollary of this and Theorem 28 of Section 7.

§ 11. Convolutions and Characteristic Functions

The integral $\int \beta(x-y)dF$, when it exists as a Lebesgue-Stieltjes integral with respect to the function $F(y)$ of bounded variation in every finite interval, is called the **convolution** of β with respect to F. If F is of bounded variation in $(-\infty, \infty)$, the convolution exists for every x if β is a bounded Borel function. We are particularly interested in this case and there is plainly no loss of generality in supposing that $F(x)$ increases and $\lim_{x \to -\infty} F(x) = 0$, $\lim_{x \to \infty} F(x) = 1$. Such functions are called **distribution functions** and are of fundamental importance in probability theory. The essential property of a distribution function is that the measure defined by it in $\mathscr{R}$ is a probability measure with $F(\mathscr{R}) = 1$. The convolution $F_1*F_2(x) = \int F_1(x-y)dF_2$ of one distribution function with respect to another is defined for all x and we consider in the next few theorems the basic properties of convolutions of this kind.

THEOREM 10. *If F_1, F_2 are distribution functions, so is $F = F_1*F_2$.*

First, it is obvious that $F(x)$ increases. If we take any point of continuity a of $F_2(x)$, we have

$$F(x) \geqq \int_{-\infty}^a F_1(x-y)dF_2(y) \geqq F_1(x-a)F_2(a) \geqq 0$$

while

$$F(x) = \int_{-\infty}^a F_1(x-y)dF_2(y) + \int_a^\infty F_1(x-y)dF_2(y)$$
$$\leqq F_2(a) + F_1(x-a)\{1 - F_2(a)\} \leqq 1,$$

and therefore

$$F_2(a) \leqq \lim_{x \to \infty} F(x) \leqq 1, \quad 0 \leqq \lim_{x \to -\infty} F(x) \leqq F_2(a),$$

and the conclusion follows.

D

THEOREM 11. *If F_1, F_2 are distribution functions and m their product measure in (x_1, x_2), the convolution operations $F_1 * F_2(x \pm 0)$ are commutative and associative and*

$$F_1 * F_2(x+0) = F_2 * F_1(x+0) = m\mathscr{E}\{x_1 + x_2 \leqq x\},$$

$$F_1 * F_2(x-0) = F_2 * F_1(x-0) = m\mathscr{E}\{x_1 + x_2 < x\}.$$

By Fubini's Theorem (33 of Chapter 2),

$$F_1 * F_2(x+0) = \int F_1(x-x_2+0)dF_2(x_2) = \int dF_2(x_2) \int_{-\infty}^{x-x_2+0} dF_1(x_1)$$

$$= \iint_{x_1+x_2 \leqq x} dF_1(x_1)dF_2(x_2) = m\mathscr{E}\{x_1 + x_2 \leqq x\}.$$

The same arguments can be applied with $x-0$ replacing $x+0$, and the extension to three variables gives

$$F_1 * (F_2 * F_3)(x+0) = (F_1 * F_2) * F_3(x+0) = m\mathscr{E}\{x_1 + x_2 + x_3 \leqq x\},$$

m now being the triple product measure.

The theorem is true in the slightly simpler form with x in place of $x+0$ provided that x is either a point of continuity or a normalised discontinuity, but this is not important in practice since we are usually concerned only with the measure defined by a distribution function and this is not affected by its values at discontinuities.

THEOREM 12. *If F_1, F_2 are distribution functions and F_1 is absolutely continuous with derivative f_1 a.e., then $F = F_1 * F_2$ is absolutely continuous and $f(x) = F'(x) = \int f_1(x-y)dF_2(y)$ a.e. If F_2 is also absolutely continuous with derivative f_2 a.e., then*

$$f(x) = \int f_1(x-y)f_2(y)dy \quad a.e.$$

By Theorem 9, we have

$$F(x) = \int F_1(x-y)dF_2(y) = \int dF_2(y) \int_{-\infty}^{x-y} f_1(t)dt$$

$$= \int dF_2(y) \int_{-\infty}^{x} f_1(t-y)dt = \int_{-\infty}^{x} dt \int f_1(t-y)dF_2(y)$$

by Fubini's theorem, provided that we show that $f_1(t-y)$ is measurable with respect to the product of F_2 and Lebesgue measure. This is certainly true for a simple function, and if L is defined in relation to the product measure, it is easy to deduce that $L\{g(t-y)\} = \int |g| dt$ for any integrable g, and that

$$L\{|f_1(t-y) - \theta_n(t-y)|\} = \int |f_1 - \theta_n| dt$$

for any sequence of simple functions θ_n. Since f_1 is integrable, these can be defined so that the right-hand side tends to 0, and the integrability and measurability of f_1 in the product space follows from Theorems 9 and 22 of Sections 6 and 7.

Hence $F'(x) = \int f_1(x-y)dF_2(y)$ a.e. by Theorem 9 again. The second part follows from Theorem 30 of Section 7.

THEOREM 13. *Suppose that F_1, F_2 are distribution functions, $F = F_1 * F_2$ and α is a bounded Borel function. Then $\int \alpha(x+y)dF_2(y)$ is integrable with respect to $F_1(y)$ and*

$$\int dF_1(y) \int \alpha(x+y)dF_2(x) = \int \alpha(x)dF(x).$$

Suppose first that $\alpha(x)$ is the characteristic function of the interval $a \le x < b$. The left hand side is then

$$\int dF_1(y) \int_{a-y-0}^{b-y-0} dF_2(x) = \int [F_2(b-y-0) - F_2(a-y-0)]dF_1(y)$$

$$= F(b-0) - F(a-0) = \int \alpha dF.$$

The theorem therefore holds in this case and extends immediately to simple functions and, after Theorem 20 of Section 6, to countable sums of non-negative simple functions. We can define a sequence of simple functions θ_n so that $|\alpha - \theta_n| \le \lambda_n$, λ_n is a countable sum of non-negative simple functions and $\int \lambda_n dF \to 0$, $\int \theta_n dF \to \int \alpha dF$.

It follows from this and Fubini's theorem, since λ_n is measurable with respect to the product measure of F_1 and F_2, that

$$\int \int \lambda_n(x+y)dF_1dF_2 = \int \lambda_n dF \to 0.$$

But if we define L with respect to this product measure,

$$L\{[\alpha(x+y) - \theta_n(x+y)]\} \le \int \int \lambda_n(x+y)dF_1dF_2 = o(1),$$

and $\alpha(x+y)$ is integrable and measurable with respect to the product measure by Theorems 9 and 22 of Sections 6 and 7. We can therefore use Fubini's theorem again, and deduce that

$$\int dF_1(y) \int \alpha(x+y)dF_2(x) = \int \int \alpha(x+y)dF_1dF_2$$
$$= \lim \int \theta_n(x+y)dF_1dF_2 = \lim \int \theta_n dF = \int \alpha dF.$$

Since e^{itx} is bounded and measurable with respect to any distribution function $F(x)$, we can define the **characteristic function** $\phi(t)$ of $F(x)$ by

$$\phi(t) = \int e^{itx}dF,$$

and we devote the remaining part of this section to the derivation of those properties of characteristic functions which are of importance in the theory of Probability.

THEOREM 14. *A characteristic function $\phi(t)$ is uniformly continuous for all t and* $\left|\phi(t)\right| \leqq 1$, $\phi(0) = 1$, $\phi(-t) = \overline{\phi(t)}$.

If we write $\phi(t+h) - \phi(t) = \int e^{itx}(e^{ihx} - 1)dF$, then

$$\left|\phi(t+h) - \phi(t)\right| \leqq \int \left|e^{ihx} - 1\right| dF = o(1)$$

as $h \to 0$, by Theorem 18 of Section 6, since $\left|e^{ihx} - 1\right| \leqq 2$. Next

$$\left|\phi(t)\right| = \left|\int e^{itx}dF\right| \leqq \int \left|e^{itx}\right| dF = \int dF = 1,$$

$$\phi(0) = \int dF = 1,$$

$$\phi(-t) = \int e^{-itx}dF = \overline{\phi(t)}.$$

THEOREM 15. *If ϕ_1, ϕ_2 are characteristic functions of F_1, F_2, respectively, then $\phi_1 \phi_2$ is the characteristic function of $F_1 * F_2$.*

$$\phi_1(t)\phi_2(t) = \int e^{ity}dF_1(y) \int e^{itx}dF_2(x)$$
$$= \int dF_1(y) \int e^{it(x+y)}dF_2(x) = \int e^{itx}d(F_1 * F_2)$$

by Theorem 13 with $\alpha(x) = e^{itx}$.

THEOREM 16. *(Inversion formulae.) Let ϕ be the characteristic function of a normalised distribution function F.*

(i) *Then for any real x and α*

$$F(x) - F(\alpha) = \lim_{A \to \infty} \frac{i}{2\pi} \int_{-A}^{A} \left[e^{-itx} - e^{-it\alpha}\right] \frac{\phi(t)}{t} \, dt.$$

(ii) *If $\delta > 0$ and*

$$F^\delta(x) = \frac{1}{2\delta} \int_{x-\delta}^{x+\delta} F(u)du,$$

then

$$F^\delta(x) - F^\delta(\alpha) = \frac{i}{2\pi\delta} \int \left[e^{-itx} - e^{-it\alpha}\right] \frac{\sin \delta t\phi(t)}{t^2} \, dt.$$

COROLLARY. *A distribution function is determined uniquely by its characteristic function.*

We assume, without loss of generality, that $x > \alpha$. Then by Theorem 33 of Section 8, we have

$$\int_{-A}^{A} \left[e^{-itx} - e^{-it\alpha}\right] \frac{\phi(t)}{t} \, dt = \int_{-A}^{A} \left[e^{-itx} - e^{-it\alpha}\right] \frac{dt}{t} \int e^{ity}dF(y)$$

$$= 2i \int dF(y) \int_{0}^{A} \left[\sin t(y-x) - \sin t(y-\alpha)\right] \frac{dt}{t}$$

$$= 2i \int \{S[A(y-x)] - S[A(y-\alpha)]\}dF(y), \tag{1}$$

where

$$S(u) = \int_0^u \frac{\sin t}{t} \, dt.$$

Moreover, it is familiar that $S(u)$ is bounded and that $S(u) \to \pm \dfrac{\pi}{2}$ according as $u \to \pm \infty$. It follows that the integrand in (1) is bounded and tends to $-\pi$ for $\alpha < y < x$, to $-\frac{1}{2}\pi$ for $y = \alpha$ or $y = x$ and to 0 for $y < \alpha$ and $y > x$. It then follows from Theorem 18 of Section 6 that the integral tends to

$$-2\pi i \int_{\alpha+0}^{x-0} dF(y) - \pi i [F(x+0) - F(x-0) + F(\alpha+0) - F(\alpha-0)]$$

$$= -2\pi i [F(x) - F(\alpha)]$$

as $A \to \infty$, and this establishes (i).

To prove (ii), we deduce from (i) that

$$\frac{i}{2\pi} \int_{-A}^{A} [e^{-itx} - e^{-it\alpha}] e^{-ith} \frac{\phi(t)}{t} \, dt \to F(x+h) - F(\alpha+h)$$

for $-\delta \leq h \leq \delta$ and observe from (1) that the integral is bounded in this range for all A. It then follows from Theorem 18 of Section 6 that

$$F^{\delta}(x) - F^{\delta}(\alpha) = \lim_{A \to \infty} \frac{i}{4\pi\delta} \int_{-\delta}^{\delta} dh \int_{-A}^{A} [e^{-itx} - e^{-it\alpha}] e^{-ith} \frac{\phi(t)}{t} \, dt$$

$$= \lim_{A \to \infty} \frac{i}{2\pi\delta} \int_{-A}^{A} [e^{-itx} - e^{-it\alpha}] \sin \delta t \, \frac{\phi(t)}{t^2} \, dt,$$

from which (ii) follows since the integrand in the last integral is plainly integrable in $(-\infty, \infty)$.

The next two theorems deal with sequences of distribution functions $F_n(x)$ and their characteristic functions $\phi_n(t)$. It is found that the most significant mode of convergence of $F_n(x)$ to a limiting distribution function $F(x)$ is that $F_n(x) \to F(x)$ at every point of continuity of $F(x)$, and we use the notation $F_n \to F$ to denote this.

THEOREM 17. *If F_n, F are distribution functions with characteristic functions ϕ_n, ϕ, and if $F_n \to F$, then $\phi_n(t) \to \phi(t)$ uniformly in any finite interval.*

If $\varepsilon > 0$, we can choose an interval I and positive integer N so that

$$\int_{I'} dF < \tfrac{1}{2}\varepsilon, \quad \int_{I'} dF_n < \tfrac{1}{2}\varepsilon \text{ for } n \geq N_0.$$

Moreover, since each F_n has at most a countable set of discontinuities, we may assume that F and F_n are continuous at the end points of I. Then since $|e^{itx}| = 1$, it follows from Theorem 5 of Section 5 and Theorem 18 of Section 6 that

$$| \phi_n(t) - \phi(t) | \leqq \varepsilon + \left| \int_I e^{itx} d(F_n - F) \right|$$

$$\leqq \varepsilon + \left| [e^{itx} F_n(x) - F(x)]_I \right| + |t| \int_I | F_n(x) - F(x) | \, dx$$

$$= \varepsilon + o(1).$$

THEOREM 18. *If ϕ_n is the characteristic function of the distribution function F_n for $n = 1, 2, 3, \ldots$ and if $\phi_n \to \phi$ for all t, where ϕ is continuous at 0, then ϕ is the characteristic function of a distribution function F and $F_n \to F$.*

Let $F(x) = \lim \sup F_n(x)$ as $n \to \infty$, so that $F(x)$ increases and $0 \leqq F(x) \leqq 1$ in $-\infty < x < \infty$. By Theorem 16 (ii),

$$F_n(2D) - F_n(-2D) \geqq F_n^D(D) - F_n^D(-D) = \frac{1}{\pi} \int \left(\frac{\sin t}{t} \right)^2 \phi_n \left(\frac{t}{D} \right) dt,$$

and since $\phi_n \to \phi$ and $|\phi_n| \leqq 1$, it follows from Theorem 18 of Chapter 2 that

$$F(2D) - F(-2D) \geqq \frac{1}{\pi} \int \left(\frac{\sin t}{t} \right)^2 \phi \left(\frac{t}{D} \right) dt$$

for any positive D. Since $\phi(t)$ is continuous at 0 and $\phi(0) = 1$, it follows again from Theorem 18 of Section 6 on letting $D \to \infty$ that $F(\infty) - F(-\infty) \geqq 1$, and $F(x)$ is therefore a distribution function.

Now let α, x be any real numbers and let $\delta > 0$. It follows from Theorem 16 (ii) that $F_n^\delta(x) - F_n^\delta(\alpha)$ tends to a limit as $n \to \infty$. If $\varepsilon > 0$, we can choose α so that $F(\alpha + \delta) < \varepsilon$, and since $\lim \inf F_n^\delta(\alpha) \geqq 0$, it then follows that

$$\lim \sup F_n^\delta(x) - \lim \inf F_n^\delta(x) \leqq \lim \sup F_n^\delta(\alpha) \leqq F(\alpha + \delta) < \varepsilon.$$

Since this holds for every positive ε, the left hand side must vanish and $\lim \sup F_n^\delta(x) = \lim \inf F_n^\delta(x)$. Hence, since $F_n(x)$ increases with x,

$$F_n(x - 2\delta) \leqq F_n^\delta(x - \delta) \leqq F_n(x),$$

$$F(x - 2\delta) \leqq \lim \sup F_n^\delta(x - \delta) = \lim \inf F_n^\delta(x - \delta) \leqq \lim \inf F_n(x).$$

This is true for every positive δ and so $F(x-0) \leqq \lim \inf F_n(x)$ and, together with the definition of $F(x)$, is enough to show that $F_n \to F$.

§ 12. CONVOLUTIONS AND CHARACTERISTIC FUNCTIONS IN $\mathscr{R}_k$

The theory of convolutions and characteristic functions in the last section can be extended, at the expense of some complication in the analysis but with no essentially new principle, to functions of more than one variable.

It is less convenient in this general case to use the idea of a distribution function, and we therefore assume that μ_1, μ_2 are two probability measures in $\mathscr{R}_k$. Then if I is any figure and $I-y$ is the figure consisting of those points x for which $(x+y)\varepsilon I$, it is clear that $\mu_1(I-y)$ is a bounded Borel function in y and is therefore integrable with respect to μ_2. If we write

$$\mu(I) = \int \mu_1(I-y)d\mu_2,$$

there is no difficulty in showing that $\mu(I)$ is completely additive and that the Lebesgue extension of it is a probability measure. We shall call this measure the **convolution** of the probability measures μ_1 and μ_2 and denote it by $\mu = \mu_1 * \mu_2$. The extension of Theorems 12 and 13 (with μ_1, μ_2 interpreted as measures rather than point functions) needs only obvious modifications.

The characteristic function $\phi(t) = \phi(t_1, t_2, ..., t_k)$ of a probability measure μ in $\mathscr{R}_k$ is defined by

$$\phi(t) = \int e^{it'x}d\mu.$$

where $t'x = \sum_{j=1}^{k} t_j x_j$ is the scalar product of t and x (regarded as column vectors to conform with the usual notation).

The formulation and proof of the k-dimensional analogues of Theorems 14 and 15 is then quite straightforward, and we can complete the extension of Section 11 by giving the general form of the inversion and limit theorems.

THEOREM 19.   *Let $\phi(t)$ be the characteristic function of a probability measure μ in $\mathscr{R}_k$. Then if I is the rectangle $a_j \leqq x_j < b_j$ ($j = 1, 2, ..., k$),*

$$\mu(I) = \lim_{\varepsilon \to 0} \int ... \int \prod_{j=1}^{k} q_j(\varepsilon, t_j)\phi(t)dt_1 dt_2 ... dt_k,$$

where

$$q_j(\varepsilon, t_j) = (2\pi\varepsilon t^2)^{-1}(e^{it\varepsilon}-1)(e^{-itb_j}-e^{-ita_j}), \quad \varepsilon > 0.$$

COROLLARY.   *A probability measure in $\mathscr{R}_k$ is defined uniquely by its characteristic functions.*

The proof is based on the elementary formula

$$Q(\varepsilon, x) = \int e^{itx}(2\pi\varepsilon t^2)^{-1}(e^{it\varepsilon}-1)(e^{-itb}-e^{-ita})dt,$$

where
$$Q(\varepsilon, x) = (x-a+\varepsilon)/\varepsilon \quad \text{for } a-\varepsilon \leqq x < a,$$
$$= 1 \quad \text{for } a \leqq x \leqq b-\varepsilon,$$
$$= (b-x)/\varepsilon \quad \text{for } b-\varepsilon \leqq x \leqq b,$$
$$= 0 \quad \text{for } x \leqq a-\varepsilon \text{ and } x \geqq b.$$

For it is easy to show that

$$\int \cdots \int \prod_{j=1}^{k} q_j(\varepsilon, t_j)\phi(t)dt_1 dt_2 \ldots dt_k = \int \prod_{j=1}^{k} Q_j(\varepsilon, x_j)d\mu,$$

and since the integrand on the right is bounded and tends to $\gamma_I(x)$, the conclusion follows from Theorem 18 of Section 6.

The idea of convergence of sequences of probability measures μ_n and their characteristic functions $\phi_n(t)$ is a natural extension of that of the last section. We say that a probability measure μ_n converges to a probability measure μ and write $\mu_n \to \mu$, if $\mu_n(I) \to \mu(I)$ for every rectangle I.

THEOREM 20. *If μ_n and μ are probability measures in R_k and ϕ_n, ϕ their characteristic functions, and if $\mu_n \to \mu$, then $\phi_n(t) \to \phi(t)$ uniformly in any finite rectangle.*

The proof of Theorem 17 extends with only trivial changes.

THEOREM 21. *If ϕ_n is the characteristic function of the probability measure μ_n for $n = 1, 2, \ldots$ and if $\phi_n \to \phi$ for all t, where ϕ is continuous at 0, then ϕ is the characteristic function of a probability measure μ and $\mu_n \to \mu$.*

The proof of Theorem 18 can be modified to cover this case if we define (as the analogue of the distribution function in the case $k = 1$) the point functions $F(b_1, b_2, \ldots, b_k)$, $F_n(b_1, b_2, \ldots, b_k)$ by the μ and μ_n measures of the set $\mathscr{E}\{x_1 < b_1, \ldots, x_k < b_k\}$.

Chapter 4

RANDOM VARIABLES AND PROBABILITY

§ 13. Definitions and Basic Ideas

The application of the foregoing theory of measure to the study of probability is based on the principle, first enunciated in its present form by Kolmogoroff †, that all statements involving the notion of probability can be expressed as statements about the measures of sets in an appropriate space. Our first task is to show how this can be done.

The basic terms are **random variable** and **probability**, and we must either define them or give a precise meaning to every sentence in which they occur. All that is necessary if we adopt the second alternative is that we understand the two sentences

(i) x is a random variable in the space $\mathscr{X}$,

(ii) the probability that x belongs to X is p or, in symbols, $P\{x \in X\} = p$

to mean that a **probability measure** (or **probability distribution**) μ is defined in $\mathscr{X}$, that X is measurable and that $\mu(X) = p$. There is no need to deal with the sentences (i) and (ii) separately since it is invariably found that (i) is followed by one or more statements, which may be hypotheses or conclusions, of type (ii). In fact, from this point of view it is not necessary to go any further and say what a random variable *is*—any more than it is necessary to define the isolated symbol ∞ in analysis.

This has been done, however, by Kolmogoroff in the case of random variables in the space $\mathscr{R}$ of real numbers. He says that a random real variable is a real valued function over a space $\mathscr{X}$ which is measurable with respect to a probability measure in $\mathscr{X}$. After Theorem 31 of Section 7, the measure in $\mathscr{X}$ induces a probability measure in $\mathscr{R}$ and this could equally well be used as the basic measure of the random variable, which would then become (in Kolmogoroff's usage) the identity function over $\mathscr{R}$. Conversely, a probability measure in $\mathscr{R}$

† A. Kolmogoroff, *Grundbegriffe der Wahrscheinlichkeitsrechnung*, Berlin, 1933.

immediately defines through the identity function a random variable in Kolmogoroff's sense.

If we recall that the terms probability and random variable never occur in isolation, but only in the context described above, there is no need to distinguish between the two ways of introducing them. The one chosen here is conceptually simpler in that it does not need the idea of a measurable function or even a function.

When $\mathscr{X}$ is a particular space of a familiar kind, it is usually convenient to show this by indicating the nature of the random variable. Thus, we speak of a **random integer** when $\mathscr{X}$ is a set of integers, a **random real number** when $\mathscr{X}$ is $\mathscr{R}$ and a **random k-vector** when $\mathscr{X}$ is $\mathscr{R}_k$. A random real number, whether restricted to integral values or not, is therefore defined by the distribution function or the characteristic function of its probability distribution in R, and we therefore speak of the **distribution** or **characteristic function** of a random real variable.

We are concerned in this section with general concepts relating to random variables which do not depend on specific properties of the space $\mathscr{X}$, although we shall use special cases quite freely for illustration.

Many problems in probability involve more than one random variable, and when these can be treated separately and without reference to one another, no new idea is required. But very often we have to consider them together within a common framework, and rather more care is then needed. We say that x_1, x_2, ..., x_k are random variables over spaces $\mathscr{X}_1, \mathscr{X}_2, ..., \mathscr{X}_k$, respectively, if $x = (x_1, x_2, ..., x_k)$ is a random variable in their product space $\mathscr{X} = \mathscr{X}_1 \otimes \mathscr{X}_2 \otimes ... \otimes \mathscr{X}_k$. The probability distribution $\mu(X)$ of x in $\mathscr{X}$ is called the **joint probability** distribution of $x_1, x_2, ..., x_k$. The sets X_1 of $\mathscr{X}$, for which $X_1 \otimes \mathscr{X}_2 \otimes ... \otimes \mathscr{X}_k$ is measurable with respect to μ, clearly form a σ-ring in $\mathscr{X}_1$ on which there is a probability $\mu_1(X_1)$ defined by

$$\mu_1(X_1) = \mu(X_1 \otimes \mathscr{X}_2, ..., \mathscr{X}_k),$$

and we can therefore say that x_1 is a random variable in $\mathscr{X}_1$ with probability distribution μ_1. In the same way, x_2, ..., x_k are random variables in $\mathscr{X}_2$, ..., $\mathscr{X}_k$, with distributions μ_2, ..., μ_k, respectively.

If μ is the product measure of measures in $\mathscr{X}_1$, ..., $\mathscr{X}_k$, these measures must clearly be μ_1, μ_2, ..., μ_k, and we say then that the random variables x_1, ..., x_k are **independent**. Otherwise, they are called **dependent**. The number of variables is assumed here to be finite. The extension to infinite sets of variables involves deeper ideas and is postponed until Chapter 5.

There is no difficulty in giving examples of independent or dependent variables. The probability distribution over the unit square

$$0 \leqq x_1 \leqq 1, \quad 0 \leqq x_2 \leqq 1$$

in which $\mu(X)$ for a Borel set is its ordinary Lebesgue measure clearly satisfies the condition for independence. On the other hand, the random variables x_1, x_2 which can take only values 0 and 1 are not independent if their joint probability distribution is defined by

$$P\{x_1 = 0, x_2 = 0\} = 0, \quad P\{x_1 = 1, x_2 = 1\} = \tfrac{1}{2},$$

$$P\{x_1 = 0, x_2 = 1\} = P\{x_1 = 1, x_2 = 0\} = \tfrac{1}{4}.$$

We have seen in Section 7 that if a function $y = \alpha(x)$ maps $\mathscr{X}$ on to $\mathscr{Y}$, the sets Y of $\mathscr{Y}$ which are inverse images of sets X, which are measurable with respect to a probability measure μ in $\mathscr{X}$, form a σ-ring in $\mathscr{Y}$, and we get a probability distribution v in $\mathscr{Y}$ by defining $v(Y) = \mu(X)$ for the (v-measurable) sets Y for which $Y = \alpha^{-1}(X)$ and X is μ-measurable. We therefore speak of a random variable y as the **function $\alpha(x)$ of a random variable** x to mean that

$$P\{y \in Y\} = v(Y) = \mu(X).$$

In order that the σ-ring of measurable sets in y is not trivial, it is usually necessary to impose some conditions on the function α. In the particularly important case of a real valued function for which $\mathscr{Y} = \mathscr{R}$, the measurability of $\alpha(x)$ in the sense of Section 7 is enough to ensure that $v(Y)$ is defined at least for all Borel sets Y.

In the following examples we suppose that $\mathscr{X} = \mathscr{Y} = \mathscr{R}$ and that x has distribution function $F(x)$ and characteristic function $\phi(t)$, and we determine the distribution and characteristic functions $G(y)$, $\psi(t)$ of $y = \alpha(x)$.

Example 1. $y = \alpha(x) = x^2$.

Since $y \geq 0$ for all x, it is plain that $G(y) = 0$ for $y < 0$. If $y \geq 0$, we must have

$$G(u+0) = P\{y \leq u\} = P\{x^2 \leq u\} = P\{-u^{\frac{1}{2}} \leq x \leq u^{\frac{1}{2}}\}$$

$$= F(u^{\frac{1}{2}}+0) - F(-u^{\frac{1}{2}}-0),$$

and since the probability measure defined by $G(y)$ is independent of its values at discontinuities, we can define

$$G(y) = F(y^{\frac{1}{2}}) - F(-y^{\frac{1}{2}}),$$

and it then follows that

$$\psi(t) = \int e^{ity} dG(y) = \int_0^\infty e^{ity} d[F(y^{\frac{1}{2}}) - F(-y^{\frac{1}{2}})] = \int e^{itx^2} dF(x).$$

Example 2. $y = \alpha(x) = x^{-1}$.

Since y must be defined with probability 1, we must have $P\{x = 0\} = 0$ and $F(x)$ must be continuous at 0. Moreover, $y \neq 0$ for real x and so $P\{y = 0\} = 0$. If $u < 0$,

$$G(u+0) = P\{y \leqq u\} = P\{x^{-1} \leqq u\} = P\{u^{-1} \leqq x < 0\} = F(0) - F(u^{-1} - 0),$$

and if $u > 0$,

$$G(u+0) = P\{y < 0\} + P\{0 < y \leqq u\} = P\{x < 0\} + P\{x \geqq u^{-1}\}$$
$$= F(0) - 1 - F(u^{-1} - 0),$$

and we can therefore write

$$G(y) = F(0) - F(y^{-1}) \quad \text{or} \quad G(y) = F(0) + 1 - F(y^{-1})$$

according as $y < 0$ or $y > 0$. Also,

$$\psi(t) = -\int_{-\infty}^{0} e^{ity} dF(y^{-1}) - \int_{0}^{\infty} e^{ity} dF(y^{-1})$$

$$= \int_{0}^{\infty} e^{itx^{-1}} dF(x) + \int_{-\infty}^{0} e^{itx^{-1}} dF(x) = \int e^{itx^{-1}} dF(x).$$

Example 3. $y = \alpha(x) = Ax + B$.

$$G(y+0) = P\{Ax + B \leqq y\} = P\{x \leqq (y-B)/A\} = F[(y-B)/A + 0]$$

if $A > 0$,

$$G(y+0) = P\{Ax + B \leqq y\} = P\{x \geqq (y-B)/A\} = 1 - F[(y-B)/A - 0]$$

if $A < 0$; and we can write $G(y) = F[(y-B)/A]$ or $1 - F[(y-B)/A$ according as $A > 0$ or $A < 0$. In both cases it follows easily that $\psi(t) = e^{itB} \phi(At)$.

The idea of several random variables $y_1, \ldots, y_k$ defined simultaneously as functions $y_1 = \alpha_1(x), \ldots, y_k = \alpha_k(x)$ of the same random variable x contains nothing essentially new. We merely define the function $y = (y_1, y_2, \ldots, y_k) = [\alpha_1(x), \ldots, \alpha_k(x)] = \alpha(x)$ mapping $\mathscr{X}$ on to the product space $\mathscr{Y} = \mathscr{Y}_1 \otimes \ldots \otimes \mathscr{Y}_k$. The distribution of $y_1, y_2, \ldots, y_k$, and questions of dependence or independence can be treated in the way described above.

We can now introduce two important **parameters** associated with random real variable. The first, called the **mean** or **expectation** of random variable x with distribution function F is denoted by $E\{x\}$ and defined by $E\{x\} = \int x dF$ whenever the integral exists in the Lebesgue sense. The definition extends readily, as the following theorem shows, to the mean of a real or complex valued function of a random variable in any space.

THEOREM 1. *If $y = \alpha(x)$ is a measurable real or complex valued function of a random variable x with distribution μ in a space $\mathcal{X}$, then*

$$E\{y\} = E\{\alpha(x)\} = \int_{\mathcal{X}} \alpha(x)d\mu$$

provided that the last integral exists.

For the theorem simply says that $\int y\,dG = \int_{\mathcal{X}} \alpha(x)d\mu$, where $G(y)$ is the distribution function of y, and this follows immediately from Theorem 31 of Section 7. Under these circumstances, we say that $\alpha(x)$ has a finite mean and use the notation $E\{y\}$ only when this is the case.

If we replace $\alpha(x)$ by $e^{it\alpha(x)}$, we deduce immediately the following general result which has already been illustrated in the examples above.

THEOREM 2. *The characteristic function $\psi(t)$ of a real-valued function $\alpha(x)$ of a random variable x with distribution μ in a space $\mathcal{X}$ is given by*

$$\psi(t) = E\{e^{it\alpha(x)}\} = \int e^{it\alpha(x)}d\mu.$$

In particular, if x is a real variable with distribution function F, then

$$\psi(t) = \int e^{it\alpha(x)}dF.$$

The second parameter σ is called the **standard deviation** of x and its square is called the **variance** of x. They are defined by

$$\sigma^2 = E\{(x-m)^2\}, \text{ where } m = E\{x\}.$$

THEOREM 3. *If x is a random real variable, then*

$$\sigma^2 = E\{(x-m)^2\} = \int (x-m)^2 dF = E\{x^2\} - m^2.$$

After Theorem 2, we need only observe that

$$\int (x-m)^2 dF = \int (x^2 - 2mx - x^2)dF = \int x^2 - 2m \int x\,dF + m^2 \int dF.$$

THEOREM 4 (*Tchebysheff's inequality*). *If $\alpha(x)$ is a non-negative real valued function of a random variable x in any probability space $\mathcal{X}$, and if $k > 0$, then $kP\{\alpha(x) \geq k\} \leq E\{\alpha(x)\}$.*

If μ is the probability distribution of x, we have

$$E\{\alpha(x)\} = \int_{\mathcal{X}} \alpha(x)d\mu \geq \int_{\alpha(x) \geq k} \alpha(x)d\mu \geq k \int_{\alpha(x) \geq k} d\mu = kP\{\alpha(x) \geq k\}.$$

The special case in which x is a random real variable and

$$\alpha(x) = (x-m)^2, \quad k = \lambda^2\sigma^2$$

is worth stating separately.

THEOREM 5. *If a random variable x has mean m and standard deviation σ, and if λ > 0, then*

$$P\{\,|\,x-m\,| \geqq \lambda\sigma\} \leqq \lambda^{-2}.$$

§ 14. RANDOM REAL NUMBERS

The practical applications of probability to statistical and other problems are based predominantly on the theory of distributions in $\mathscr{R}_k$, and we shall devote this chapter to an account of this in the simplest and most familiar space $\mathscr{R}$ and deal rather more systematically with the properties of random real numbers and their distribution and characteristic functions.

Two special types are of particular interest. First, if a distribution function $F(x)$ is absolutely continuous, its derivative $f(x) = F'(x)$ exists almost everywhere and is called the **probability density** of the random variable.

In the second type, we have

$$F(x+0) = \sum_{\lambda_v \leqq x} p_v, \quad p_v > 0, \quad \sum_{v=0}^{\infty} p_v = 1.$$

We say in this case that $F(x)$ is a **point distribution function**. It is plain that $F(x)$ is a step function if the points λ_v are isolated, and this is necessarily the case when their number is finite. But they need not be isolated, and in this case $F(x)$ is not a step function. It is possible, for example, for λ_v to include the dense set of rationals or any other countable set.

THEOREM 6. *If x is a random real number with point distribution function F, then $P\{x = \lambda_v\} = p_v$, $P\{x \neq \lambda_v$ for all $v\} = 0$. Moreover, if α(x) is a measurable function of x, it has finite mean*

$$E\{\alpha(x)\} = \sum_{v=0}^{\infty} p_v \alpha(\lambda_v)$$

provided that the series converges absolutely. In particular, the characteristic function φ(t) of x is given by

$$\phi(t) = \sum_{v=0}^{\infty} p_v e^{it\lambda_v}.$$

We have

$$P\{x = \lambda_v\} = F(\lambda_v + 0) - F(\lambda_v - 0)$$

$$= \lim_{\delta \to 0} \sum_{\lambda_v - \delta < \lambda_j < \lambda_v + \delta} p_j = p_v,$$

since every point λ_j other than λ_v is excluded from the interval $\lambda_v - \delta < x < \lambda_v + \delta$ when δ is sufficiently small. Since $\Sigma p_v = 1$, it follows that $P\{x \neq \lambda_v \text{ for all } v\} = 1 - \Sigma p_v = 0$, and after Theorem 1, it follows that

$$E\{\alpha(x)\} = \int \alpha(x)dF = \sum_{v=0}^{\infty} \int_{x = \lambda_v} \alpha(x)dF = \sum_{v=0} p_v\alpha(\lambda_v).$$

In the practically important case in which x is a random integer and the numbers λ_v are all non-negative integers, we may suppose that $\lambda_v = v$ if we admit zero values of p_v when necessary. In this case,

$$\phi(t) = \sum_{v=0}^{\infty} p_v e^{itv} = p(e^{it}),$$

where $p(z)$, defined for all complex z in the unit circle $|z| \leq 1$ by

$$p(z) = \sum_{v=0}^{\infty} p_v z^v,$$

is called the **probability generating function** of the distribution.

If we are dealing only with random integers, probability generating functions can be used instead of characteristic functions, and the theory can be based on the elementary properties of power series rather than the more elaborate analysis of Chapter 3.

If m is the mean of a random real number, we define † μ_j, called the j-th **moment of x about its mean**, or the j-th **central moment**, by

$$\mu_j = E\{(x-m)^j\},$$

so that $\mu_0 = 1$, $\mu_1 = 0$, $\mu_2 = \sigma^2$, and the mean and moments can all be expressed immediately in terms of the distribution function.

It is also sometimes useful to express them as we do in the next two theorems in terms of the characteristic function or, in the case of random integers, the probability generating function.

THEOREM 7. *If a random real number x has a finite mean, then its characteristic function $\phi(t)$ is differentiable at $t = 0$ and*

$$m = E\{x\} = -i\phi'(0).$$

If it has a finite j-th moment and $j \geq 2$, then $\phi(t)$ has a j-th derivative at $t = 0$ and

$$\mu_j = \sum_{v=0}^{j} \binom{j}{v} m^{j-v} i^v \phi^{(v)}(0), \quad \sigma^2 = \mu_2 = [\phi'(0)]^2 - \phi''(0).$$

If $h \neq 0$, we have

$$\phi(t+h) - \phi(t) = \int e^{itx}[e^{ihx} - 1]dF,$$

† This is the usual notation, and we choose to retain it in spite of the previous use of μ in the quite unrelated sense of a measure.

and since $(e^{ihx}-1)/h \to ix$ as $h \to 0$ and $|e^{ihx}-1| \leq |hx|$ for all real x and h, the conclusion follows from Theorem 18 of Section 6.

If the j-th moment exists, a similar argument shows that the equation

$$\phi(t)e^{-itm} = \int e^{it(x-m)}dF$$

can be differentiated formally j times to give

$$\mu_j = (-i)^j D^j [\phi(t)e^{-itm}]_{t=0} = \sum_{v=0}^{j} \binom{j}{v} m^{j-v} i^v \phi^{(v)}(0).$$

The formula for σ^2 is simply the case $j = 2$.

THEOREM 8. *If n is a random integer with probability generating function $p(\xi)$ and finite mean m, then $p(\xi)$ has left derivative m at 1. If n has a finite second moment, $p(\xi)$ has a left second derivative and $\sigma^2 = \mu_2 = p''_-(1) + p'_-(1) - [p'_-(1)]^2$. If $p(\xi)$ is once or twice differentiable at 1, the derivatives can be taken in the ordinary two-sided sense.*

If $m = \Sigma v p_v < \infty$ and $0 \leq \xi < 1$, we have

$$\lim_{\xi \to 1-0} \frac{p(1)-p(\xi)}{1-\xi} = \lim_{\xi \to 1-0} \sum_{v=0}^{\infty} p_v \frac{1-\xi^v}{1-\xi} = \sum_{v=0}^{\infty} v p_v,$$

since $(1-\xi^v)/(1-\xi) = 1+\xi+\xi^2+\dots\xi^{v-1}$ increases and tends to v as $\xi \to 1-0$ and $\Sigma v p_v$ converges.

If the second moment is finite, $\Sigma v^2 p_v < \infty$ and if $0 \leq \xi < 1$,

$$p''(1) = \lim \frac{p'(1)-p'(\xi)}{1-\xi} = \lim_{\xi \to 1-0} \sum_{v=0}^{\infty} v p_v \frac{(1-\xi^{v-1})}{1-\xi}$$

$$= \sum_{v=0}^{\infty} v(v-1)p_v = \sum_{v=0}^{\infty} v^2 p_v - \sum_{v=0}^{\infty} v p_v = \sigma^2 + m^2 - m.$$

There are several other parameters of a random real number which are also used, though less frequently than the mean and standard deviation; and we touch on them only very briefly. First, **a median** of the random variable with distribution function F is any number q for which $F(q-0) \leq \frac{1}{2} \leq F(q+0)$. A median always exists since the condition is obviously satisfied by the upper bound of the real members x for which $F(x) \leq \frac{1}{2}$, but it is not unique when $F(x) = \frac{1}{2}$ in an open interval $q_1 < x < q_2$, for the median values there are the points q of the closed interval $q_1 \leq q \leq q_2$.

The number $\frac{1}{2}$ used in defining the median may be replaced by any number p in the range $0 < p < 1$, and a number q_p so defined that $F(q_p-0) \leq p \leq F(q_p+0)$ is called the **quantile of order p** of the distribution. The values $p = \frac{1}{4}, p = \frac{3}{4}$ give **upper and lower quartiles**, and the interval $q_{\frac{1}{4}} \leqq x \leqq q_{\frac{3}{4}}$ is called the **interquartile range**. The quartiles, like the median, are not necessarily unique, but they often give a good account of the magnitude and spread of a random variable.

A distribution is said to have a finite **range** $[r, R]$ if $F(r-0) = 0$, $F(R+0) = 1$ and $0 < F(x) < 1$ for $r < x < R$, so that $P\{r \leqq x \leqq R\} = 1$. In particular, a variable taking only a finite number of values has a range in which r is the least and R the greatest.

The **absolute moment** $E\{|x-c|\}$ **about a point** c is occasionally used instead of the standard deviation as a measure of spread. The following theorem shows that it is related to the median, as is the standard deviation to the mean, by an interesting minimal property.

THEOREM 9. (i) *The mean square deviation* $E\{(x-c)^2\}$ *about a number* c *has the strict minimum value of* σ^2 *when* $c = m$. (ii) *The absolute moment* $E\{|x-c|\}$ *about a number* c *has the same value* [*called the* **mean deviation**] *for all median values* c *and a greater value when* c *is not a median*.

To prove (i), we observe that

$$E\{(x-c)^2\} = \int (x-c)^2 dF = \int (x-m+m-c)^2 dF$$
$$= \int (x-m)^2 dF + 2(m-c) \int (x-m)dF + (m-c)^2 \int dF$$
$$= \sigma^2 + (m-c)^2,$$

and the conclusion is obvious.

In (ii), if $c < q$, and q is a median,

$$E\{|x-c|\} - E\{|x-q|\} = \int (|x-c| - |x-q|)dF = q - c - 2\int_c^q F(x)dx$$

by partial integration. This vanishes if c is also a median value, since then $F(x) = \frac{1}{2}$ in $c < x < q$. But if c is not a median value, $F(x) < \frac{1}{2}$ in a proper subinterval of $c < x < q$, $\int_c^q F(x)dx < \frac{1}{2}(q-c)$, and $E\{|x-c|\} > E\{|x-q|\}$. A similar argument applies when $c > q$.

It is useful at this point to define some of the more familiar distributions and their properties.

The singular distribution

In the limiting case in which a variable takes a value λ with probability 1, F has a single discontinuity at λ and is defined by

$$F(x) = 0 \ (x < \lambda), \quad F(x) = 1 \ (x > \lambda).$$

It follows immediately that $\phi(t) = 1$, $m = \lambda$, $\sigma = 0$.

The binomial distribution

If $0 < p < 1$, $q = 1 - p$ and n is a positive integer, a random integer is

E

said to have a binomial distribution (n, p) if it takes the value v with probability

$$p_v = \binom{n}{v} p^v q^{n-v} \ (v = 0, 1, 2, ..., n), \quad p_v = 0 \ (v > n).$$

Then
$$m = np, \quad \sigma^2 = npq, \quad p(x) = (q+px)^n,$$

$$\phi(t) = \sum_{v=0}^{n} \binom{n}{v} p^v q^{n-v} e^{itv} = (q+pe^{it})^n.$$

The Poisson distribution

The random integer can take all non-negative integral values v with probabilities $p_v = e^{-c} c^v / v!$, where c is a positive constant. It follows immediately that $m = c, \sigma^2 = c$,

$$p(x) = e^{c(x-1)}, \quad \phi(t) = e^{-c(e^{it}-1)}.$$

The Poisson distribution function can be regarded as the limiting form of the binomial distribution function when $pn = c$ is constant and n is large. For then

$$p_v = \binom{n}{v} p^v q^{n-v} = \frac{n(n-1)...(n-v+1)}{v!} \frac{c^v}{n^v} \left(1 - \frac{c}{n}\right)^{-v} \left(1 - \frac{c}{n}\right)^n$$

$$= \frac{e^{-c} c^v}{v!} + o(1)$$

as $n \to \infty$ for each fixed v.

These three examples are all of discrete distributions. The four that follow are absolutely continuous and can be defined by their probability densities $F'(x) = f(x)$.

The rectangular distribution

The probability density of the **rectangular** or **uniform** distribution on an interval (a, b) is defined by $f(x) = (b-a)^{-1} (a \leq x \leq b), f(x) = 0$ elsewhere. Then plainly $m = q = \frac{1}{2}(a+b), \sigma^2 = (b-a)^3/12$,

$$\phi(t) = \frac{1}{b-a} \int_a^b e^{itx} dt = \frac{e^{itb} - e^{ita}}{it(b-a)}.$$

The normal (or Gaussian) distribution

We say that the distribution of a random real variable is **normal** (m, σ) if its probability density is given by

$$f(x) = (2\pi\sigma^2)^{-\frac{1}{2}} e^{-(x-m)^2/2\sigma^2}.$$

The fact that $\int f(x)dx = 1$ follows from the elementary identity $\int_0^\infty e^{-x^2}dx = \pi^{\frac{1}{2}}$. It is plain that the median is m and it is easy to verify that the mean is m and the standard deviation σ as the notation suggests and anticipates. For

$$E\{x\} = (2\pi\sigma^2)^{-\frac{1}{2}}\int xe^{-(x-m)^2/2\sigma^2}dx$$
$$= (2\pi)^{-\frac{1}{2}}\int (x+m)e^{-x^2/2}dx = m,$$

since $xe^{-x^2/2}$ is an odd function. Further,

$$E\{(x-m)^2\} = (2\pi\sigma^2)^{-\frac{1}{2}}\int (x-m)^2 e^{-(x-m)^2/2\sigma^2}dx$$
$$= \sigma^2(2\pi)^{-\frac{1}{2}}\int x^2 e^{-x^2/2}dx = \sigma^2$$

by partial integration.

The characteristic function is given by

$$\phi(t) = (2\pi\sigma^2)^{-\frac{1}{2}}\int e^{-(x-m)^2/2\sigma^2 + itx}dx$$
$$= e^{itm-t^2\sigma^2/2}(2\pi)^{-\frac{1}{2}}\int e^{-(x+it\sigma)^2}dx,$$

and a simple contour integration shows that the integral is equal to $\int e^{-x^2/2}dx = (2\pi)^{\frac{1}{2}}$, and so $\phi(t) = e^{itm-t^2\sigma^2/2}$.

The Cauchy distribution

The density distribution given by $f(x) = a[\pi(x^2+a^2)]^{-1}$ with $a > 0$ has median 0 but no mean and no finite standard deviation since $xf(x)$, $x^2f(x)$ are not integrable. It has characteristic function

$$\phi(t) = \frac{a}{\pi}\int \frac{e^{itx}}{x^2+a^2} = \frac{1}{\pi}\int \frac{e^{itax}}{x^2+1} = e^{-a|t|},$$

again by a simple contour integration.

The Gamma and χ^2 distributions

The Gamma (l) distribution is defined for $l > 0$ by the density

$$f(x) = [\Gamma(l)]^{-1}e^{-x}x^{l-1} \quad (x > 0),$$
$$= 0 \quad\quad\quad\quad\quad\quad (x \leqq 0),$$

and we have

$$E\{x\} = \Gamma(l+1)/\Gamma(l) = l.$$

The characteristic function can be shown to be

$$\phi(t) = \frac{1}{\Gamma(l)}\int_0^\infty e^{-x(1-it)}x^{l-1}dx = (1-it)^{-l}$$

by a simple contour integration.

The χ^2 distribution of order k, for any positive integer k, is of great practical importance in Statistics. It has density

$$f_k(x) = 2^{-k/2}[\Gamma(k/2)]^{-1}e^{-x/2}x^{k/2-1} \quad (x>0),$$

$$= 0 \qquad\qquad\qquad\qquad (x\leqq 0),$$

and characteristic function

$$\psi_k(t) = [\psi_1(t)]^k = (1-2it)^{-k/2}.$$

It is, in fact, the distribution of $2x$ when x has a Gamma $(k/2)$ distribution.

§ 15. RANDOM REAL VECTORS

A random real vector $x = (x_1, x_2, ..., x_k)$ is defined by a probability measure μ in $\mathscr{R}_k$ which determines the joint distributions of its components $x_1, x_2, ..., x_k$. These are independent or not according as μ is or is not the product measure of k probability measures $\mu_1, \mu_2, ..., \mu_k$ in $\mathscr{R}$. There is no satisfactory analogue in $\mathscr{R}_k$ of the distribution function, which plays so useful a role in the one-dimensional case. However, there are two extreme types of the kind mentioned in the last section and which still merit a distinctive notation when they occur. First, we have a **point distribution** if a random vector can take only values λ_v of a countable set and if positive probabilities $p_v = \boldsymbol{P}\{x = \lambda_v\}$, with $\Sigma p_v = 1$, are assigned. In particular, if the components of λ_v all have non-negative integral values, the distribution can be defined by its **probability generating function**

$$p(\xi) = \sum_{v_i \geqq 0} p_v \xi_1^{v_1} \xi_2^{v_2} ... \xi_k^{v_k}.$$

At the other extreme, if μ is absolutely continuous, it has a non-negative derivative $f(x)$ by the Radon-Nikodym theorem such that

$$\boldsymbol{P}[x\in X\} = \int_X f(x)dx = \int ... \int_X f(x_1, x_2, ..., x_k)dx_1...dx_k$$

for every Borel measurable set X. The function $f(x)$ is naturally called the **probability density function** of x.

Many of the ideas and results of the last section can now be extended in a natural way to the k-dimensional case. The **mean** of a random vector x is the vector $m = (m_1, m_2, ..., m_k)$ defined by

$$m = \boldsymbol{E}\{x\} = \int x d\mu, \quad m_j = \int x_j d\mu$$

in the general case and takes the form $m = \Sigma \lambda_v p_v$ for a point distribution. More generally, if $\alpha(x)$ is any measurable vector valued function of x (not necessarily of the same dimension as x), its mean is given by

$$E\{\alpha(x)\} = \int \alpha(x)d\mu$$

whenever this integral exists. If the components of x are independent, this takes the form

$$E\{\alpha(x)\} = \int \dots \int \alpha(x)d\mu_1 \dots d\mu_k.$$

In particular, the case $\alpha(x) = x_1 \ x_2 \ \dots \ x_k$ gives immediately the following.

THEOREM 10. *If $x_1, x_2, \dots, x_k$ are independent and have finite means $m_1, m_2, \dots, m_k$, then $x_1 x_2 \dots x_k$ has finite mean $m_1 m_2 \dots m_k$. That is,*

$$E\{\Pi x_j\} = \Pi E\{x_j\}.$$

If the vector x has a density $f(x)$, we have

$$E\{\alpha(x)\} = \int \dots \int \alpha(x) f(x)dx_1 \dots dx_k,$$

and if the components are also independent in this case it is easy to see that $f(x) = f_1(x) \dots f_k(x)$, where $f_1, f_2, \dots, f_k$ are density functions over $\mathcal{R}$, and

$$E\{\alpha(x)\} = \int \dots \int \alpha(x) f_1(x_1) \dots f_k(x_k)dx_1 \dots dx_k.$$

Other cases in which the values of $\alpha(x)$ are real numbers are important and include the familiar **parameters** of a random vector. Thus, the **moment of order** $j_1, j_2, \dots, j_k$ of x **about its mean** is defined by

$$\mu_{j_1, j_2, \dots, j_k} = E\{(x_1 - m_1)^{j_1} \dots (x_k - m_k)^{j_k}\} = \int (x_1 - m_1)^{j_1} \dots (x_k - m_k)^{j_k}d\mu.$$

The second order moments are particularly important. Since $j_i = 0$ except for one or two values of i, it is customary to use a slightly different notation and write

$$\mu_{ij} = E\{(x_i - m_i)(x_j - m_j)\}, \quad \sigma_i^2 = \mu_{ii} = E\{(x_i - m_i)^2\}.$$

The matrix $M = [\mu_{ij}]$ is called the **moment matrix**, its diagonal term μ_{ii} is called the **variance** of x_i, $(\mu_{ii})^{\frac{1}{2}}$ is called the **standard deviation** of x_i. The ratio $p_{ij} = \mu_{ij}(\mu_{ii}\mu_{jj})^{-\frac{1}{2}}$ is called the **correlation coefficient** of x_i and x_j provided that $\mu_{ii} > 0$, $\mu_{jj} > 0$, and the matrix $[p_{ij}]$ which is defined when all μ_{ii} are positive, is called the **correlation matrix**. The components x_i are said to be **uncorrelated** if $\mu_{ij} = 0$ when $i \neq j$, so that the moment matrix reduces to diagonal form. The correlation matrix then reduces to the unit matrix if the variances are all positive.

The **characteristic function** $\phi(t) = \phi(t_1, t_2, \dots, t_k)$ of a random vector x is defined, as in Section 12, by

$$\phi(t) = E\{e^{it'x}\} = \int e^{it'x}d\mu.$$

where $t'x = \Sigma t_i x_i$ is the scalar product of t and x. The characteristic function of a variable with a point distribution has the form $\Sigma p_v e^{it'\lambda_v}$

which becomes $p[e^{it_1}, e^{it_2}, ..., e^{it_k}]$ when its components are non-negative integers.

Each of the variables x_i has its own characteristic function

$$\phi_i(t_i) = E\{e^{it_i x_i}\} = \int e^{it_i x_i} d\mu$$

and the relationship between these and the joint characteristic function for the vector x gives the following important criteria for independence.

THEOREM 11. *If variables $x_1, x_2, ..., x_k$ have characteristic functions $\phi_1(t_1), ..., \phi_k(t_k)$ and a joint characteristic function $\phi(t)$, a necessary and sufficient condition for independence is that $\phi(t) = \phi_1(t_1), \phi_2(t_2), ..., \phi_k(t_k)$.*

The proof is almost immediate from the definition of independence. For if $x_1, x_2, ..., x_k$ are independent,

$$\phi(t) = \int e^{it'x} d\mu = \int ... \int e^{it_1 x_1} e^{it_2 x_2} ... e^{it_k x_k} d\mu_1 ... d\mu_k$$

$$= \phi_1(t_1) ... \phi_k(t_k),$$

since

$$\phi_j(t_j) = \int ... \int e^{it_j x_j} d\mu_1 ... d\mu_k = \int e^{it_j x_j} d\mu_j.$$

Conversely, if $\phi(t) = \phi_1(t_1) ... \phi_k(t_k)$, we have

$$\phi(t) = \int e^{it_1 x_1} d\mu_1 ... \int e^{it_k x_k} d\mu_k = \int e^{it'x} d\mu,$$

where μ is the product measure of $\mu_1, \mu_2, ... \mu_k$ and is the distribution of a vector with independent components.

If x has independent components each with the same distribution μ in $\mathscr{R}$, it is usually called a **sample** of size k from a population with distribution μ, and the study of samples and distributions of functions of samples is of considerable practical importance.

In the more general case, we are usually concerned with a vector valued function of a random vector. In some cases it is enough to know its mean and other parameters, while in others we require its complete distribution. We devote the rest of this section to some general theorems and special examples relating to these ideas.

We begin with the simplest algebraic function of a vector, defined by its linear transform $y = Cx$ by a matrix C.

THEOREM 12. *If x is a random vector in $\mathscr{R}_k$ with mean m and characteristic function $\phi(t)$, C a matrix of l rows and k columns, the random l-vector defined by $y = Cx$ has mean Cm and characteristic function $\psi(u) = \phi(C'u)$.*

In particular, if $x_1, x_2, ..., x_k$ have means $m_1, m_2, ..., m_k$, their sum $x = \Sigma x_j$ has mean Σm_j, and this is true whether they are independent or not.

If μ denotes the distribution of x in $\mathscr{R}_k$, we have

$$E\{y_i\} = E\left\{\sum_{j=1}^{k} c_{ij}x_j\right\} = \int \sum_j c_{ij}x_j d\mu = \sum_j c_{ij} \int x_j d\mu$$

$$= \sum c_{ij}E\{x_j\} = \sum c_{ij}m_j,$$

and since this holds for $i = 1, 2, ..., l$, we get $E\{y\} = Cm$. Also

$$\psi(u) = E\{e^{iu'y}\} = E\{e^{iu'Cx}\} = E\{e^{i(C'u)'x}\} = \phi(C'u).$$

When the components of x are independent, we have the following important result.

THEOREM 13. *If $x_1, x_2, ..., x_k$ are independent real variables with distribution functions $F_1, F_2, ..., F_k$ and characteristic functions $\phi_1(t), ..., \phi_k(t)$, respectively, their sum has distribution function $F = F_1*F_2*...*F_k$ and characteristic function $\psi(u) = \phi_1(u)\phi_2(u)...\phi_k(u)$. Moreover, if at least one variable has a density distribution, so has their sum.*

Here the characteristic function of the vector x in $\mathscr{R}_k$ is

$$\phi(t) = \phi_1(t_1)...\phi_k(t_k)$$

by Theorem 11, and if C is the row vector $(1, 1, ..., 1)$, the last theorem gives $y = x_1+x_2+...+x_k = Cx$,

$$\psi(u) = \phi(C'u) = \phi(u, u, ..., u) = \phi_1(u)...\phi_k(u).$$

The results about the distribution functions then follow from Theorems 12 and 15 of Section 11.

There is an analogous but more elementary theorem for random integers.

THEOREM 14. *If x_1, x_2 are random non-negative integers with probability generating functions $p_1(\xi), p_2(\xi)$, then $x_1 + x_2$ has generating function $p_1(\xi)p_2(\xi)$.*

We need only observe that

$$p_v = P\{x_1+x_2 = v\} = \sum_{j=0}^{v} P\{x_1 = j, \ x_2 = v-j\}$$

$$= \sum_{j=0}^{v} p_{1,j} \, p_{2,v-j},$$

so that

$$p(\xi) = \sum_{v=0}^{\infty} p_v \xi^v = p_1(\xi)p_2(\xi).$$

The following theorem shows that sums of pairs of random variable of certain types are also of the same types.

THEOREM 15. *We suppose that x_1, x_2 are independent.* (i)
*If x_1, x_2 are binomial (n_1, p), (n_2, p), respectively, then $x_1 + x_2$ is
binomial $(n_1 + n_2, p)$.* (ii) *If x_1, x_2 are both Poisson variables with means
c_1, c_2, then $x_1 + x_2$ is Poisson with mean $c_1 + c_2$.* (iii) *If x_1, x_2 are normal
(m_1, σ_1) and (m_2, σ_2), respectively, then $x_1 + x_2$ is normal (m, σ), where
$m = m_1 + m_2$, $\sigma^2 = \sigma_1^2 + \sigma_2^2$.* (iv) *If x_1, x_2 are Gamma (l_1) and (l_2),
respectively, then $x_1 + x_2$ is Gamma $(l_1 + l_2)$.*

These follow at once from Theorem 13 and the forms of the
characteristic functions for the special distributions listed in Section 14.

The extension to quadratic functions of a random vector can be
based very conveniently on the moment matrix.

THEOREM 16. *Suppose that x is a random vector in $\mathcal{R}_k$ with moment
matrix M. Then $y = Cx$ has moment matrix CMC'.*

If we suppose that x has mean m so that $q = Cm$ is the mean of y,
the second order moments v_{ij} of y are given by

$$v_{ij} = E\{(y_i - q_i)(y_j - q_j)\}, = E\left\{ \sum_{r=1}^{k} \sum_{s=1}^{k} c_{ir} c_{js} (x_r - m_r)(x_s - m_s) \right\}$$

$$= \sum_{r=1}^{k} \sum_{s=1}^{k} c_{ir} c_{js} E\{(x_r - m_r)(x_s - m_s)\}, \quad \text{by Theorem 11,}$$

$$= \sum_{r=1}^{k} \sum_{s=1}^{k} c_{ir} c_{js} \mu_{rs},$$

which is our conclusion.

As an immediate corollary, we have

THEOREM 17. *If $x_1, x_2, ..., x_k$ are uncorrelated (in particular, if they
are independent) and have variances $\sigma_1^2, \sigma_2^2, ..., \sigma_k^2$, then their sum has
variance $\sigma_1^2 + \sigma_2^2 + ... + \sigma_k^2$.*

In this case M is diagonal, with diagonal terms σ_j^2, C is the row
vector with unit terms and the variance of $y = \Sigma x_j = Cx$ is the single
term of the 1×1 matrix CMC', which is plainly $\Sigma \sigma_j^2$.

THEOREM 18. *If x is a sample of size k from a population of mean m
and variance σ^2, the sample mean $\bar{x} = k^{-1} \Sigma x_j$ has mean m and variance
σ^2/k, and the sample variance $s^2 = k^{-1} \Sigma (x_j - \bar{x})^2$ has mean $(k-1)\sigma^2/k$.*

The mean and variance of $\bar{x}$ are given at once by Theorems 12 and
17. Using Theorem 12 again, we have

$$E\{s^2\} = \frac{1}{k} \sum_{j=1}^{k} E\{(x_j - \bar{x})^2\}.$$

But

$$x_1 - \bar{x} = \frac{1}{k}\left[(k-1)x_1 - x_2 - \ldots - x_k\right],$$

and

$$E\{(x_1 - \bar{x})^2\} = \frac{1}{k^2}\left[(k-1)^2 + (k-1)\right] = (k-1)\sigma^2/k,$$

since $E\{x_i x_j\} = 0$ when $i \neq j$ and $E\{x_j^2\} = \sigma^2$. It is plain that $E\{(x_j - \bar{x})^2\}$ has the same value for $j = 1, 2, \ldots, k$, and therefore $E\{s^2\} = (k-1)\sigma^2/k$, as required.

We now describe briefly some of the more familiar special distributions in $\mathcal{R}_k$.

The multinomial distribution $(n: p_1, p_2, \ldots, p_k)$

We suppose that $q > 0$, $p_j > 0$, $\Sigma p_j = 1 - q$, that n is a positive integer and that the components $(x_1, x_2, \ldots, x_k)$ of a random vector take non-negative integral values with probabilities defined by

$$P\{x_j = v_j, j = 1, 2, \ldots, k\} = \frac{n!}{v_1! v_2! \ldots v_k! u!}\, p_1^{v_1} p_2^{v_2} \ldots p_k^{v_k} q^u,$$

$$\text{if } u = n - \sum_j v_j \geqq 0;$$

$$= 0 \quad \text{if } u < 0.$$

The binomial distribution in $\mathcal{R}$ which was defined in the last section is obviously the case $k = 1$, $p_1 = p$, $q = 1 - p$. The distribution in the general case is in $\mathcal{R}_k$, but it may equally well be regarded, if we write $u = v_{k+1}$, $q = p_{k+1}$, as a distribution over the hyperplane $\sum_{j=1}^{k+1} x_j = n$ in $\mathcal{R}_{k+1}$.

The probability generating function $p(\xi) = p(\xi_1, \xi_2, \ldots, \xi_k)$ is given by

$$p(\xi) = \sum_{v_1 + v_2 \ldots + v_k \leqq n} \frac{n! q^u}{v_1! v_2! \ldots v_k! u!}\, (p_1 \xi_1)^{v_1} \ldots (p_k \xi_k)^{v_k}$$

$$= (q + p_1 \xi_1 + p_2 \xi_2 + \ldots p_k \xi_k)^n,$$

and the mean $m = (m_1, m_2, \ldots, m_k)$ by $m_j = \dfrac{\partial p}{\partial \xi_j}$ at the point $\xi = (1, 1, \ldots, 1)$, and this is np_j.

The characteristic function is

$$\phi(t) = p(e^{it_1}, e^{it_2}, \ldots e^{it_k}) = \left(q + \sum_{j=1}^{k} p_j e^{it_j}\right)^n.$$

The k-dimensional Poisson distribution

We suppose that $c_j > 0$ $(j = 1, 2, ..., k)$ and that $x_1, x_2 ..., x_k$ take non-negative integral values with probabilities given by

$$P\{x_j = v_j, j = 1, 2, ..., k\} = e^{-c} \frac{c_1^{v_1} c_2^{v_2} ... c_k^{v_k}}{v_1! v_2! ... v_k!},$$

where $c = \Sigma c_j$. The probability generating function is

$$p(\xi) = e^{-c} \sum_{v_j \geq 0} \frac{(c_1 \xi_1)^{v_1} (c_2 \xi_2)^{v_2} ... (c_k \xi_k)^{v_k}}{v_1! v_2! ... v_k!}$$

$$= \prod_{j=1}^{k} e^{c_j(\xi_j - 1)}.$$

The mean is defined by

$$m_j = \left(\frac{\partial p}{\partial \xi_j} \right)_{\xi = 1, 1, ..., 1} = c_j,$$

and the characteristic function is

$$\phi(t) = p(e^{it_1}, e^{it_2}, ..., e^{it_k}) = \prod_{j=1}^{k} e^{c_j(e^{it_j} - 1)}.$$

The uniform distribution over a set

If X is a measurable set of Lebesgue measure A in $\mathcal{R}_k$, the distribution with constant density $f(x) = A^{-1}$ in X and $f(x) = 0$ in X' defines a uniform distribution over X. If $k = 1$, the most natural form of X is an interval, and we get the rectangular distribution defined before. If $k \geq 2$, other forms such as circles or rectangles may occur. For example, the uniform distribution over the rectangle $| x_1 | \leq a_1, | x_2 | \leq a_2$ in $\mathcal{R}_2$ has mean 0, density function $(4a_1 a_2)^{-1}$ in the rectangle and characteristic function

$$\left(\frac{\sin a_1 t_1}{a_1 t_1} \right) \left(\frac{\sin a_2 t_2}{a_2 t_2} \right).$$

The normal distribution

We begin by defining an important special case. We say that a vector x in $\mathcal{R}_k$ has an **independent normal distribution**, with mean m and variances $\sigma_1^2, \sigma_2^2, ..., \sigma_k^2$, if its components x_j are independent and normal and have means m_j, respectively. The density of x is then plainly

$$(2\pi)^{-n/2} (\sigma_1 \sigma_2 ... \sigma_k)^{-1/2} e^{-\Sigma(x_j - m_j)^2 / 2\sigma_j^2}$$

and its characteristic function is $e^{it'm - \frac{1}{2}\Sigma t_j^2 \sigma_j^2}$.

We now define a general normal distribution by saying that x is a normal random vector in $\mathscr{R}_k$ if it can be expressed by $x = m + Cy$, where m is a constant vector in $\mathscr{R}_k$, y is an independent normal vector in $\mathscr{R}_l$ and C is a matrix of k rows and l columns. It is obvious from the definition that any linear transform of a normal vector is also normal, and the other essential properties of normal vectors and distributions are contained in the following theorems.

THEOREM 19. *The normal variable $x = m + Cy$, where y is independent in R_l with mean 0 and variances $\sigma_1^2, \sigma_2^2, \ldots, \sigma_l^2$ and C has rank r, has mean m and characteristic function $\phi(t) = e^{it'm - \frac{1}{2}t'Mt}$, where $M = CC'$ is a non-negative $k \times k$ matrix of rank r.*

We deduce immediately from Theorem 12 that the mean of x is m and that

$$\phi(t) = e^{it'm}\psi(C't),$$

where $\psi(u)$ is the characteristic function of y and has the form

$$\psi(u) = e^{-\frac{1}{2}\Sigma u_j^2 \sigma_j^2} = e^{-\frac{1}{2}u'Qu}$$

and Q has terms $\sigma_1^2, \sigma_2^2, \ldots, \sigma_l^2$ in its first l diagonal places and zeros elsewhere. We therefore have the required formula $\phi(t) = e^{it'm - \frac{1}{2}t'Mt}$ with $M = CQC'$. It is obvious from the form of M that it is symmetric, non-negative and of order k.

The following theorem is the converse.

THEOREM 20. *If M is a non-negative symmetric $k \times k$ matrix of rank r, then $\phi(t) = e^{it'm - \frac{1}{2}t'Mt}$ is the characteristic function of a normal random variable x.*

In every expression of x in the form $x = m + Cy$ in which y is an independent normal vector, the matrix C has the same rank r. Moreover, an expression of this form can be found in which $l = r$, the variances $\sigma_1^2, \sigma_2^2, \ldots, \sigma_r^2$ of y are the r positive proper values of M and C consists of the first r columns of an orthogonal matrix P.

Alternatively, we can take $x = m + P\eta$, where η is a vector in $\mathscr{R}_k$ whose first r components are independent and normal $(0, \sigma_j)$ $(j = 1, 2, \ldots, r)$ and whose remaining $k - r$ components are all zero.

The **rank of a normal vector** is defined as the common rank of all the matrices C which may be used in its definition. The vector and its distribution are called **regular** if $r = k$, $|M| > 0$ and **singular** if $r < k$, $|M| = 0$. We have as immediate corollaries.

THEOREM 21. *The rank of a normal vector is the smallest number of independent normal variables in terms of which it can be expressed linearly.*

THEOREM 22. *A normal vector of rank r lies with probability 1 in a sub-space of dimension r.*

THEOREM 23. *A normal random vector x has a density distribution if and only if it is regular. In this case, if its characteristic function is*

$$\phi(t) = e^{it'm - \frac{1}{2}t'Mt},$$

then its density function is

$$f(x) = (2\pi)^{-n/2} \left| M \right|^{-\frac{1}{2}} e^{-\frac{1}{2}(x-m)'M^{-1}(x-m)}$$

where M is the moment matrix of x, $\sigma_1^2, \sigma_2^2, ..., \sigma_k^2$ its proper values and $\left| M \right| = \sigma_1^2 \sigma_2^2 ... \sigma_k^2$.

Furthermore, we can write $x = m + Py$, where P is orthogonal and y an independent normal vector in $\mathcal{R}_k$ with mean 0 and variances σ_j^2.

By a familiar theorem on matrices, we can define an orthogonal matrix P of order k so that $M = P'QP$. Then

$$\phi(t) = e^{it'm - \frac{1}{2}t'Mt} = e^{it'm - \frac{1}{2}t'P'QPt}$$

and this, after Theorem 11, is the characteristic function of $m + Cy = m + P\eta$, where y_j are independent and normal $(0, \sigma_j)$ for $1 \leq j \leq r$ and $\eta_j = y_j$ for $1 \leq j \leq r$, $\eta_j = 0$ for $r+1 \leq j \leq k$.

The joint distribution of the Mean and Variance of a normal sample

It has been show in Theorem 18 that the mean and standard deviation of the mean $\bar{x}$ and the variance s^2 of a sample of size k from any given population can be found in terms of those of the population. It is not generally possible to go further and find the distributions of $\bar{x}$ and s, either separately or jointly, except for special populations. Among these, the normal population is particularly important in practical applications, and the next theorem gives the complete joint distribution of $\bar{x}$ and s^2 and shows that they are independent.

THEOREM 24. *If $x = (x_1, x_2, ..., x_k)$ is a sample from a normal $(0, 1)$ population, then the sample mean $\bar{x}$ and variance s^2 are independent. The mean $\bar{x}$ is normal $(0, k^{-\frac{1}{2}})$ and ks^2 has the χ^2 distribution of order $k-1$ with density $f_{k-1}(x)$ and characteristic function $\psi_{k-1}(u)$, where*

$$f_k(x) = e^{-\frac{1}{2}x} x^{\frac{1}{2}k - 1} \quad (x > 0),$$

$$= 0 \quad (x \leq 0),$$

$$\psi_k(u) = (1 - 2iu)^{-k/2} = [\psi_1(u)]^k.$$

We can define an orthogonal transformation $x = Py$ by means of an orthogonal matrix P so that $y_1, y_2, ..., y_k$ are independent,

$$y_k = k^{-\frac{1}{2}} \Sigma x_j = \bar{x} k^{\frac{1}{2}}.$$

Then

$$ks^2 = \sum_{j=1}^{k} (x_j - \bar{x})^2 = \sum_{j=1}^{k} x_j^2 - \bar{x}^2 = \sum_{j=1}^{k} y_j^2 - y_k^2,$$

by the orthogonal property of P, and so

$$ks^2 = \sum_{j=1}^{k-1} y_j^2,$$

and we get the joint characteristic function $\phi(t, u)$ of $(\bar{x}, ks^2)$ in the form

$$\phi(t, u) = E\{e^{it\bar{x} + iuks^2}\} = E\{e^{itk^{-\frac{1}{2}} y_k + iu\Sigma y_j^2}\}$$

$$= E\{e^{itk^{-\frac{1}{2}} y_k}\} \prod_{j=1}^{k-1} E\{e^{iuy_j^2}\}$$

by Theorem 12, since $y_1, y_2, ..., y_k$ are independent.   Hence

$$\phi(t, u) = e^{-t^2/2k} [\psi_1(u)]^{k-1},$$

where

$$\psi_1(u) = E\{e^{iuy^2}\} = (2\pi)^{-\frac{1}{2}} \int e^{(iu - \frac{1}{2})y^2} dy$$

$$= (2\pi)^{-\frac{1}{2}} \int_0^\infty e^{-\frac{1}{2}x(1 - 2iu)} x^{-\frac{1}{2}} dx = \int_0^\infty e^{iux} f_1(x) dx,$$

and this is $(1 - 2iu)^{-1}$ by simple contour integration.   Since $\psi_1(u)$ is the characteristic function of the density $f_1(x)$, the formula for $f_{k-1}(x)$ follows from the relation $f_k = f_{k-1} * f$, which is obvious by induction. The independence of $\bar{x}$ and s^2 is clear from the factorization of $\phi(t, u)$ into their characteristic functions $e^{-t^2/2k}$ and $\psi_{k-1}(u)$.

§ 16. Dependence and Conditional Probabilities

The idea of conditional probability can be introduced most easily by considering the product space $\mathscr{Z} = \mathscr{X} \otimes \mathscr{Y}$ of spaces $\mathscr{X}$, $\mathscr{Y}$ and supposing that a joint probability distribution λ is given for the random variable (x, y).   We know from Section 8 that this joint distribution defines probability distributions $\mu(X) = \lambda(X \otimes \mathscr{Y})$, $\nu(Y) = \lambda(\mathscr{X} \otimes Y)$ in $\mathscr{X}$, $\mathscr{Y}$, respectively, but we do not assume that these are independent.

If X, Y are measurable sets in $\mathscr{X}$, $\mathscr{Y}$, respectively, we know that $X \otimes Y$ is measurable in $\mathscr{Z}$ and if $\mu(X) > 0$, we call $\lambda(X \otimes Y)/\mu(X)$ the **conditional probability** that y belongs to Y under the condition that x belongs to X.   We denote this by $\nu(Y/X)$, so that

$$\nu(Y/X) = \frac{\lambda(X \otimes Y)}{\mu(X)}, \; (\mu(X) > 0).$$

It is clear that, for any fixed X, $v(Y/X)$ is defined in the σ-ring of measurable sets Y of $\mathcal{Y}$, and is completely additive by the complete additivity of λ. Moreover, $v(Y/X) \geqq 0$ and

$$v(\mathcal{Y}/X) = \frac{\lambda(X \otimes \mathcal{Y})}{\mu(X)} = 1,$$

so that $v(Y/X)$ is a probability measure in $\mathcal{Y}$ for each fixed X. In particular, if X reduces to a single point x with $\mu(X) > 0$, we write $v(Y/X)$ as $v(Y/x)$. By interchanging X and Y in these arguments, we have

$$\mu(X/Y) = \frac{\lambda(X \otimes Y)}{v(Y)}, \; (v(Y) > 0)$$

as the conditional probability that $x \in X$ under condition $y \in Y$, and there is complete symmetry between X and Y. In application, however, it is generally more useful to think of y as being in some sense dependent on x, and the extreme case of this arises when the value of y is strictly determined (or determined with probability 1) by that of x, and so that y is a function of x in the usual real variable sense and the whole mass of the joint distribution is concentrated in the graph $[x, y(x)]$. The values, or sets of values, of y can now be regarded as **hypotheses**, the values of x as **observations**. A conditional probability then gives the expected distribution of the observed variable under a *given* hypothesis, and experiments can often be designed so that these conditional probabilities are known for each of a system of possible hypotheses. The object of the experiment is then to use the observations of values of x to express opinions about the merits of different hypotheses or to modify any opinions which were held before the experiment took place. For this reason, the distribution μ of x is usually called the **prior probability** distribution of the hypothesis x and the conditional probability $\mu(X/Y)$ is called the **post probability** or **likelihood** of X under the observation Y.

These ideas are illustrated in the following famous result called **Bayes' Theorem**.

THEOREM 25. *Suppose that (x, y) is a random variable in the product space $\mathcal{X} \otimes \mathcal{Y}$, that Y, X_k are measurable for $k = 1, 2, 3, \ldots$, and that $v(Y) > 0$, $\mu(X_k) > 0$, $\mathcal{X} = \bigcup_{k=1}^{\infty} X_k$. Then*

$$\mu(X_k/Y) = \frac{v(Y/X_k)\mu(X_k)}{\Sigma v(Y/X_k)\mu(X_k)}.$$

This follows almost immediately from the definitions, since

$$\mu(X_k/Y)\Sigma v(Y/X_k)\mu(X_k) = \frac{\lambda(X_k \otimes Y)}{v(Y)} \Sigma\lambda(X_k \otimes Y)$$

$$= \frac{\lambda(X_k \otimes Y)}{v(Y)} \lambda(\mathscr{X} \otimes Y) = \lambda(X_k \otimes Y) = v(Y/X_k)\mu(X_k).$$

The concept of conditional probability can be put in a way which appears to be more general. If $\mathscr{Z}$ is any probability space with distribution λ, and Z_1 any measurable subset of it, we can define the conditional probability $\lambda(Z/Z_1)$ that $z \in Z$ under the condition $z \in Z_1$ to be $\lambda(Z \otimes Z_1)/\lambda(Z_1)$. The definitions used above then apply if the sets Z, Z_1 are restricted to sets of the type $x \in X$ and $y \in Y$ in a product space $\mathscr{Z} = \mathscr{X} \otimes \mathscr{Y}$. Bayes' Theorem takes the form

$$\lambda(Z_k/Z) = \frac{\lambda(Z/Z_k)\lambda(Z_k)}{\Sigma\lambda(Z/Z_k)\lambda(Z_k)}$$

when Z_k are measurable sets and $\lambda(Z_k) > 0$, $\bigcup Z_k = \mathscr{Z}$. In fact, there is no greater generality in this form since it can be put in the form of Theorem 25 by considering the product space $\mathscr{Z} \otimes \mathscr{X}$, where $\mathscr{X}$ is the space of positive integers with $P\{x = k\}$ defined to be $\lambda(Z_k)$.

We shall therefore maintain the product space form as it was first introduced and illustrate the application of Bayes' Theorem to a simple experiment.

We suppose that two boxes x_1, x_2 are offered at random with (prior) probabilities 1/3, 2/3. It is known that the box x_1 contains 8 white counters and 12 red, while x_2 contains 4 white and 4 red counters. The observer takes a counter at random from the box offered, without knowing which box it is, and finds that the counter is white. How will he assess the likelihood that the box was x_1?

Here, the **hypothesis space** $\mathscr{X}$ contains two points x_1, x_2 with probabilities $\mu(x_1) = \frac{1}{3}$, $\mu(x_2) = \frac{2}{3}$. The **observation space** $\mathscr{Y}$ also contains only two values y_1 (for a white counter), y_2 (for red). The conditional probabilities are given by the proportions of red and white counters in each box, so that

$$v(y_1/x_1) = 8/20 = 2/5, \quad v(y_1/x_1) = 4/8 = 1/2.$$

Hence, by Bayes' theorem, the likelihood that the box is x_1 is

$$\mu(x_1/y_1) = \frac{v(y_1/x_1)\mu(x_1)}{v(y_1/x_1)\mu(x_1) + v(y_1/x_2)\mu(x_2)}$$

$$= \frac{\frac{2}{5} \cdot \frac{1}{3}}{\frac{2}{5} \cdot \frac{1}{3} + \frac{1}{2} \cdot \frac{2}{3}} = \frac{2}{7}.$$

The result may be stated in terms of the frequency interpretation of probabilities by saying that in a long sequence of experiments, the proportion of offers of box x_1 in those experiments which resulted in the choice of a white counter would be 2/7.

The conditional probability $v(Y/x)$ has been defined for *points* x only when x has positive μ measure when considered as a measurable set, and it is natural to enquire whether any extension to more general cases is possible. This can be done, but rather less directly than before, through the following theorem.

THEOREM 26. *Let λ be the joint distribution of (x, y) in $\mathscr{X} \otimes \mathscr{Y}$ and let μ, v be the distributions of x, y, respectively. Then if Y is any measurable set with respect to v, there is defined for almost all x a unique function $v(Y/x)$ which is integrable over $\mathscr{X}$ with respect to μ and has the property that*

$$\lambda(X \otimes Y) = \int_X v(Y/x)d\mu$$

for every measurable X in $\mathscr{X}$. In particular,

$$v(Y) = \lambda(\mathscr{X} \otimes Y) = \int_{\mathscr{X}} v(Y/x)d\mu,$$

and $v(\mathscr{Y}/x) = 1$ for almost all x.

If we consider $\lambda(X \otimes Y)$, for fixed Y, as a set function defined on the σ-ring of measurable sets X, it is plain from the fact that $\lambda(Z)$ is a probability measure that it is completely additive. Moreover, since

$$\lambda(X \otimes Y) \leq \lambda(X \otimes \mathscr{Y}) = \mu(X),$$

it is absolutely continuous with respect to μ, and the main conclusion then follows from the Radon-Nikodym theorem (Theorem 28 of Section 7). That $v(\mathscr{Y}/x) = 1$ a.e. follows from the fact that $0 \leq v(\mathscr{Y}/x) \leq 1$ and $\mu(\mathscr{X}) = 1 = \lambda(\mathscr{X} \otimes \mathscr{Y}) = \int_{\mathscr{X}} v(\mathscr{Y}/x)d\mu$.

The number $v(Y/x)$ is called the **conditional probability** that y belongs to Y under the condition that x takes its assigned value. It is defined uniquely outside a nul set by λ, and its value is the same as that previously defined in the case when $\mu(X) > 0$. It is important to observe, however, that the nul set in $\mathscr{X}$ in which $v(Y/x)$ is not defined depends on Y, so that although the definition of $v(Y/x)$ can be extended simultaneously to any *countable* system of sets Y by excluding the countable union of all the nul sets associated with each, it cannot be done in general for non-countable systems. Above all, we cannot assume in general that, for almost all x, $v(Y/x)$ is completely additive in Y and has a measure extension. We shall return to this point later, but show at this stage that it is possible to proceed somewhat further even without any extra assumptions. First, we deduce another form of Bayes' Theorem.

THEOREM 27. *If $v(Y)>0$, the post probability $\mu(X/Y)$ under the observation Y has a density $\dfrac{v(Y/x)}{v(Y)}$ with respect to μ, and Bayes' formula can be written in the form*

$$\mu(X/Y) = \frac{\displaystyle\int_X v(Y/x)d\mu}{v(Y)} = \frac{\displaystyle\int_X v(Y/x)d\mu}{\displaystyle\int_{\mathscr{X}} v(Y/x)d\mu}$$

for every measurable set X.

This follows immediately from Theorem 26 and the definition of $v(Y/X)$ and $\mu(X/Y)$, since

$$\mu(X/Y) = \frac{\lambda(X \otimes Y)}{v(Y)} = \frac{\lambda(X \otimes Y)}{\lambda(\mathscr{X} \otimes Y)}.$$

The conditional probability $v(Y/X)$ is a measure in $\mathscr{Y}$ and if a real-valued function $\alpha(y)$ is integrable with respect to it, we have the **conditional mean** $E\{\alpha(y)/X\}$ of $\alpha(y)$ given by

$$E\{\alpha(y)/X\} = \int_{\mathscr{Y}} \alpha(y)dv(Y/X).$$

The following theorem shows that a *conditional mean* $E\{\alpha(y)/x\}$ can be defined for *points* x, in spite of the fact that $v(Y/x)$ is not generally a measure. When it is a measure, we see below that $E\{\alpha(y)/x\}$ can be expressed as an integral in the normal way.

THEOREM 28. *Suppose that $\alpha(y)$ is integrable with respect to v. Then it is integrable with respect to $v(Y/X)$ whenever X is measurable and $\mu(X)>0$. Moreover, there is defined for almost all x a unique function $E\{\alpha(y)/x\}$ which is integrable over $\mathscr{X}$ with respect to μ and has the property that*

$$E\{\alpha(y)/X\} = \int_{\mathscr{Y}} \alpha(y)dv(Y/X) = \frac{1}{\mu(X)}\int_X E\{\alpha(y)/x\}d\mu$$

whenever $\mu(X)>0$. In particular, if $X = \mathscr{X}$,

$$E\{\alpha(y)\} = E\{\alpha(y)/\mathscr{X}\} = \int_{\mathscr{X}} E\{\alpha(y)/x\}d\mu.$$

If $\alpha(y)$ is the characteristic function of a measurable set Y, then $E\{\alpha(y)/X\} = v(Y/X)$, $E\{\alpha(y)/x\} = v(Y/x)$, and the theorem reduces to Theorem 26.

If $\alpha(y)$ is the characteristic function of a measurable set Y and $\mu(X) > 0$, $v(Y) > 0$, we have

$$\mu(X) \int_{\mathcal{Y}} \alpha(y)dv(Y/X) = \mu(X)v(Y/X) = \lambda(X \otimes Y) = \int_{X \otimes \mathcal{Y}} \alpha(y)d\lambda$$

and the same is obviously true for any simple function $\alpha(y)$. Also, we have

$$\mu(X) \int |\alpha(y)| \, dv(Y/X) \leqq \int |\alpha(y)| \, dv$$

for every simple function $\alpha(y)$, since $\mu(X)v(Y/X) = \lambda(X \otimes Y) \leqq v(Y)$ for every Y. This is enough to ensure that any function $\alpha(y)$ which is integrable with respect to v is also integrable over $\mathcal{Y}$ with respect to $v(Y/X)$ and over $\mathcal{Z}$ with respect to λ, and that

$$\mu(X)E\{\alpha(y)/X\} = \mu(X) \int \alpha(y)dv(Y/X) = \int_{X \otimes \mathcal{Y}} \alpha(y)d\mu.$$

This is true, in particular, when $X = \mathcal{X}$, and therefore $\int_Z \alpha(y)d\lambda$ is absolutely continuous and bounded over the σ-ring of measurable sets Z in $\mathcal{Z}$. It is then absolutely continuous over the σ-ring of sets of the form $X \otimes \mathcal{Y}$ and it follows from the Radon-Nikodym theorem that $\int_{X \otimes \mathcal{Y}} \alpha(y)d\lambda$ is the integral over X of a function $E\{\alpha(y)/x\}$ which is defined uniquely almost everywhere and is integrable in $\mathcal{X}$. The conclusions of the theorem follow at once.

The next theorem deals with the case in which the conditional probabilities $v(Y/x)$ can be extended into probability measures and shows that the expressions $E\{\alpha(y)/x\}$ can be expressed as integrals with respect to $v(Y/x)$ in the usual sense.

THEOREM 29. *Suppose that for almost all x a probability measure $v_x(Y)$ can be defined on the measurable sets Y of $\mathcal{Y}$ to satisfy*

$$\lambda(X \otimes Y) = \int_X v_x(Y)d\mu$$

for every measurable X. Then if Y is any measurable set, $v_x(Y) = v(Y/x)$ for almost all x, and if $\alpha(x, y)$ is integrable in $\mathcal{Z}$, then $\alpha(x, y)$ is integrable in $\mathcal{Y}$ with respect to v_x for almost all x and

$$E\{\alpha(x, y)\} = \int \alpha(x, y)d\lambda = \int_{\mathcal{X}} \left\{ \int_{\mathcal{Y}} \alpha(x, y)dv_x \right\} d\mu.$$

In particular, if $\alpha(y)$ is integrable with respect to v, it is integrable with respect to v_x and

$$E\{\alpha(y)/x\} = \int \alpha(y)dv_x$$

for almost all x.

Moreover, the distribution is independent if and only if $v_x(Y) = v(Y)$ for almost all x.

The first part is obvious from the fact that

$$\int_X v(Y/x)d\mu = \lambda(X \otimes Y) = \int_X v_x(Y)d\mu$$

and

$$\int_X [v(Y/x) - v_x(Y)]d\mu = 0 \quad \text{for every } X.$$

For the next part, we suppose first that $\alpha(x, y)$ is the characteristic function of a set $X \otimes Y$, when X, Y are both measurable. Using Theorem 26, we have $v(Y/x) = \int_Y \alpha(x, y)dv_x$, and

$$\int_X v(Y/x)d\mu = \int\left\{\int \alpha(x, y)dv_x\right\} d\mu = \int \alpha(x, y)d\lambda = \lambda(X \otimes Y)$$

and this extends immediately to simple functions, and for such functions we have also

$$\int\left\{\int |\alpha(x, y)| dv_x\right\} d\mu \leqq \int |\alpha(x, y)| d\lambda.$$

This is enough to ensure, by the approximation to $\alpha(x, y)$ by simple functions, that $\int |\alpha(x, y)| dv_x$ exists for almost all x if $\alpha(x, y)$ is a general integrable function over $\mathscr{L}$, and there is then no difficulty in extending the formula

$$\int\left\{\int \alpha(x, y)dv_x\right\} d\mu = \int \alpha(x, y)d\lambda$$

from simple functions to the general case. The special form

$$E\{\alpha(y)/x\} = \int \alpha(y)dv_x$$

follows by taking $\alpha(x, y) = \alpha(y)$.

Finally, if $v_x = v$ for almost all x, we have

$$\lambda(X \otimes Y) = \int_X\left\{\int_Y dv_x\right\} d\mu = \int_X v(Y)d\mu = \mu(X)v(Y)$$

for every measurable X and Y, and the distribution is independent. Conversely, if this condition is given, it follows for any given Y that

$$\int_X v_x(Y)d\mu = \lambda(X \otimes Y) = \mu(X)v(Y)$$

and therefore $v_x(Y) = v(Y)$ for almost all x.

The following theorem shows that the conditional probability measures v_x exist, and the conditions of the last theorem hold, when $\mathscr{Y}$ (but not necessarily $\mathscr{X}$) is a real vector space $\mathscr{R}_k$.

THEOREM 30. *If $\mathscr{Y} = \mathscr{R}_k$, a probability measure v_x can be defined on $\mathscr{Y}$ for almost all x to satisfy the conditions of Theorem* 29.

It is enough to give the proof when $k = 1$. The same argument, then extends without essential change, but with minor complications to the general case. We define $v(I/x)$ for all simple sets I consisting of unions of finite numbers of intervals $a \leq y < b$ with rational end points. Since the system of all these simple sets is countable, the set of points x to be excluded in the definition of $v(Y/x)$ for all of them can remain a nul set. If I_1, I_2 are two simple sets, we have

$$\int_X v(I_1 \cup I_2/x)d\mu = \lambda(I_1 \cup I_2 \otimes X) = \lambda(I_1 \otimes X) + \lambda(I_2 \otimes X)$$

$$= \int_X [v(I_1/x) + v(I_2/x)]d\mu$$

for every measurable X, and therefore

$$v(I_1 \cup I_2/x) = v(I_1/x) + v(I_2/x)$$

for almost all x. Since the finite additivity of $v(I/x)$ over the simple sets can be expressed by a countable number of relations of this kind, we may suppose that for almost all x, $v(I/x)$ is finitely additive. The *complete* additivity of $v(I/x)$ can now be expressed by a countable set of conditions of the type $v(I_n/x) \to v(I/x)$ for almost all x, where $I_n \uparrow 1$. This follows for any one simple set and the sequence I_n associated with it from the fact that

$$\int_X [v(I/x) - v(I_n/x)]d\mu = \lambda(\mathscr{X} \otimes I) - \lambda(\mathscr{X} \otimes I_n)$$

$$= v(I - I_n) = o(1) \text{ as } h \to \infty$$

and $v(I/x) - v(I_n/x)$ is non-negative and decreasing as $n \to \infty$ for almost all x and so has limit zero by Theorem 20 of Section 6.

The theorem remains true for more general spaces, although we shall have no occasion to use the fact. It is sufficient that $\mathscr{Y}$ should be a topological space and that its measure should be an extension of an additive set function over a countable ring of simple sets each containing a compact set of measure arbitrarily close to its own.

After Theorem 30, the theory of dependence between variables x and y in real vector spaces can be developed in more concrete terms and it becomes useful to introduce a number of concepts and parameters which have a clear practical significance. It is enough to illustrate this in the case in which x and y are both single real numbers. The extensions to higher dimensions are more complicated but involve no basically new ideas.

We can assume then that the conditional probability v_x is defined for almost all x and that the conditional mean $m(x)$ is defined by

$$m(x) = E\{y/x\} = \int y \, dv_x.$$

The graph $y = m(x)$ is called the **regression curve of y on x**. It has an interesting minimal property in the cases when y has a finite variance.

THEOREM 31. *Suppose that (x, y) has a joint distribution in which y has a finite variance. Then the conditional distribution of y has finite variance $\sigma(x)$ for almost all x, and the regression function $y = m(x)$ of x on y is the function which minimises $E\{[y-q(x)]^2\}$ for all real functions $y = q(x)$.*

The existence of $\sigma(x)$ for almost all x follows from Theorem 29, from which we also deduce, by putting $\alpha(x, y) = [y-q(x)]^2$, that

$$E\{[y-q(x)]^2\} = \int \left\{ \int [y-q(x)]^2 dv_x \right\} d\mu.$$

Since $\int [y-q(x)]^2 dv_x$ is obviously least, for each fixed x, when $q(x) = m(x)$, the conclusion follows.

The number $E\{[y-m(x)]^2\}$ is the mean square deviation of y from its conditional mean, and gives a measure of the deviation of the distribution from the *completely determinate* state in which y takes a single assigned value with probability 1 for every x. The **correlation ratio** θ of y on x is defined by $\theta^2 = 1 - \sigma^{-2} E\{[y-m(x)]^2\}$ and obviously lies between 0 and 1 and approaches the value 1 for a distribution with y concentrated near to its regression line.

The problem of choosing the function $y = q(x)$ to minimise $E\{[y-q(x)]^2\}$ takes a different form if instead of allowing a choice of

$y(x)$ for *all* functions of x, we restrict the choice to some specified class. Among these classes the polynomials of given degree are most commonly used, and the polynomial $p_r(x)$ of degree r for which $E\{[y-p_r(x)]^2\}$ is minimum defines the **polynomial regression curve** $y = p_r(x)$ of y on x. The **linear regression** given by the case $r = 1$ is particularly important, and it is possible in this case to carry the analysis rather further. We consider polynomials $p(x) = a + bx$ with arbitrary a and b, and find that

$$E\{[y-p(x)]^2\} = E\{[y-a-bx]^2\}$$
$$= E\{[y-m-b(x-l)+m-bl-a]^2\},$$

where (l, m) is the mean of (x, y) for the whole distribution. This gives

$$E\{[y-p(x)]^2\} = E\{(y-m)^2\} - 2bE\{(x-l)(y-m)\}$$
$$+ bE\{(x-l)^2\} + (m-bl-a)^2$$

and this is plainly least when $b = \rho\sigma/\tau$, $a = m - l\rho\sigma/\tau$, where $\sigma^2 = E\{(y-m)^2\}$, $\tau^2 = E\{(x-l)^2\}$ and ρ is the regression coefficient $E\{(x-l)(y-m)\}/\sigma\tau$. The linear regression line is therefore

$$y = p_1(x) = m + \rho\sigma(x-l)/\tau.$$

The actual minimal value of $E\{[y-p(x)]^2\}$, attained when $y = p_1(x)$ is the linear regression line, has the value $\sigma^2(1-\rho^2)$. The total variance σ^2 of y can be expressed as the sum of two components in the form

$$\sigma^2 = E\{(y-m)^2\} = E\{(y-m(x))^2\} + E\{(m(x)-m)^2\}$$
$$= \sigma^2(1-\theta^2) + \sigma^2\theta^2,$$

where θ is the correlation ratio. The two terms on the right are the components of the variance due respectively to the deviation of y from its conditional mean and the deviation of the conditional mean from the overall mean m. The first term is therefore the residual variance which remains after as great a component as possible has been removed by a determinate function $y = m(x)$. A small value of this residual, given by a value of θ near to 1, indicates that the distribution is closely concentrated near a single curve $y = m(x)$. A smaller value of θ indicates that the random component is larger.

The total variance cannot be expressed in quite the same way for linear regressions, but we still have the residual variance $\sigma^2(1-\rho^2)$ when the variance has been reduced by the greatest possible amount by the subtraction from y of a linear term $a + bx$. This vanishes if and only if the whole distribution is concentrated on a line and there is a determinate *linear* relationship between y and x.

The condition that ρ is near to ± 1 therefore has a precise and explicit interpretation, but no such clear cut interpretation is possible for other values. In particular, the variables are said to be **uncorrelated** when $\rho = 0$, and it is obvious that independent variables are uncorrelated but that the converse is not generally true. In fact, $\rho = 0$ means that the linear regression is parallel to the x-axis, and this is a much weaker condition than independence. Moreover, except in the cases when $|\rho|$ is near to 1, the value of ρ gives little information about the deviation of y from the determinate form. For example $\rho = 0$ if y takes the value $\cos x$ with probability 1 for every x in the interval $-\pi \leqq x \leqq \pi$.

Chapter 5

LIMIT PROCESSES IN PROBABILITY

Limit processes may arise in several different ways from sequences of random variables. In the simplest of these, to which we devote the rest of this section, we are concerned simply with the limiting behaviour of a sequence of distribution functions, and there is no need to consider the joint distributions of the associated random variables, although these may exist and be known.

The appropriate form of convergence is that in which the sequence of distribution functions $F_n(x)$ converges to a distribution function $F(x)$ at every continuity point of the latter, and we denote this property by writing $F_n \to F$. After Theorems 17 and 18 of Section 11, we know that this is equivalent to the convergence for all t of the sequence of characteristic functions $\phi_n(t)$ to a function $\phi(t)$ continuous at 0.

It is important to observe that the notion of a limiting *random variable* need not appear, but if we do wish to relate the behaviour of random variables x_n to such a limit variable x, it is necessary to define the joint distributions of (x, x_n) for every n. There are two important definitions based on this. We say that a random real variable x_n **converges in probability** to x, and write $x_n \to x$ **in probability**, if

$$\lim_{n \to \infty} P\{|x_n - x| > \eta\} = 0$$

for every positive η, P being the joint probability in the product spaces of x and x_n.

It is plain that $x_n \to x$ in probability means that $x_n - x \to 0$ in probability, and this can be expressed in terms of the distribution functions of $x_n - x$. In particular, if C is a constant, $x_n \to C$ in probability is equivalent to the condition that $F_n \to D_c$, where $D_c(x) = D(x - C)$, and

76

$D(x)$ is the singular distribution function with a single discontinuity of magnitude 1 at $x = 0$.

The second definition is of mean convergence. We say that x_n **converges in mean of order** $p(p \geq 1)$ to a random variable x if the distribution of $x_n - x$ is known from the joint distribution of (x, x_n), if $E\{|x|^p\}$, $E\{|x_n|^p\}$ are finite for every n and if

$$\lim_{n \to \infty} E\{|x_n - x|^p\} = 0.$$

It is clear that this is equivalent to saying that $x_n - x$ converges in mean to 0. In particular, $x_n \to 0$ in mean is equivalent to

$$\lim_{n \to \infty} \int |x|^p dF_n = 0.$$

Before discussing the general theory of convergence of distribution functions, we mention some well known and simple special cases.

THEOREM 1.   (i) *If* $x_n \to x$ *in probability, then* $F_n \to F$. (ii) *If* $x_n \to x$ *in mean of order* p, *then* $x_n \to x$ *in probability.*

Let a be a point of continuity of $F(x)$. Let $\varepsilon > 0$ and define η so that $F(a + \eta + 0) \leq F(a) + \varepsilon$. Then we can choose N so that

$$P\{|x - x_n| > \eta\} \leq \varepsilon$$

for $n \geq N$. Thus, for $n \geq N$,

$$P\{x_n \leq a\} + P\{x > a + \eta\} \leq 1 + P\{x_n \leq a, \ x > a + \eta\}$$
$$\leq 1 + P\{|x_n - x| > \eta\} \leq 1 + \varepsilon,$$
$$F_n(a) \leq F_n(a + 0) = P\{x_n \leq a\}$$
$$\leq 1 - P\{x > a + \eta\} + \varepsilon$$
$$= P\{x \leq a + \eta\} + \varepsilon$$
$$= F(a + \eta + 0) + \varepsilon \leq F(a) + 2\varepsilon.$$

A similar argument shows that $F_n(a) \geq F(a) - 2\varepsilon$, and the conclusion (i) follows.

Part (ii) follows from the inequality

$$E\{|x_n - x|^p\} \geq \varepsilon^p P\{|x_n - x| > \varepsilon\}.$$

THEOREM 2 (*Tchebycheff*).   *If* x_n *has mean* m_n *and standard deviation* σ_n, *and if* $\sigma_n \to 0$, *then* $x_n - m_n \to 0$ *in probability.*

This follows directly from the case $p = 2$ of Theorem 1 (ii).

THEOREM 3 (*Bernoulli's weak law of large numbers*).   *Let* $\xi_1, \xi_2, \ldots$

be independent random real numbers with standard deviations σ_1, σ_2, ...
and let

$$x_n = \frac{1}{n} \sum_{v=1}^{n} \xi_v, \quad m_n = E\{x_n\} = \sum_{v=1}^{n} E\{\xi_v\}.$$

Then $x_n - m_n \to 0$ *in probability if* $\sum_{v=1}^{n} \sigma_v^2 = o(n^2)$.

The conditions ensure that $x_n - m_n$ has mean 0 and standard deviation tending to 0, and the conclusion then follows from Tchebycheff's inequality (Theorem 4 of Section 13).

THEOREM 4 (*Khintchine*). *If* ξ_1, ξ_2, ... *are independent random real numbers with the same distribution and finite mean m, then*

$$x_n = \frac{1}{n} \sum_{v=1}^{n} \xi_v \to m$$

in probability.

(We notice first that this does not follow from Theorem 3, since the variables ξ_v are not assumed to have finite variances.)

Let $\phi(t)$, $F(x)$ be the characteristic and distribution functions of ξ_v, so that the characteristic function of x_n is $[\phi(t/n)]^n$ and

$$\phi(t) = 1 + itm + \int(e^{itx} - 1 - itx)dF.$$

Since $|(e^{itx} - 1 - itx)/t|$ is less than $2|x|$ for all t, and tends to 0 for every fixed x, as $t \to 0$, it follows from the Lebesgue convergence theorem (Theorem 18 of Section 6) that $\phi(t) = 1 + itm + o(t)$ and that

$$\left[\phi\left(\frac{t}{n}\right)\right]^n = \left[1 + \frac{itm}{n} + o\left(\frac{t}{n}\right)\right]^n \to e^{itm}$$

for every t as $n \to \infty$. Since e^{itm} is the characteristic function of $D(x-m)$, the conclusion follows.

THEOREM 5 (*Poisson*). *Let* F_n *be the distribution function of a random integer* x_n *with a binomial distribution given by* $P\{x_n = v\} = \binom{n}{v} p_n^v q_n^{n-v}$,
where $0 < p_n < 1$, $q_n = 1 - p_n$, $p_n = c/n$ *and c is a positive constant. Then* $F_n \to F$, *where F is the Poisson distribution function with mean c.*

The characteristic function of F_n is

$$\phi_n(t) = (q_n + p_n e^{it})^n = \left\{1 + \frac{c(e^{it}-1)}{n}\right\}^n$$

$$= e^{c(e^{it}-1)} + o(1), \quad \text{as } n \to \infty,$$

which is sufficient since this is the Poisson characteristic function.

THEOREM 6 (*De Moivre*). *If* ξ_1, ξ_2, ... *are independent random real numbers with the same distribution and characteristic functions* $F(x)$ *and* $\phi(t)$, *with mean* 0 *and finite standard deviation* σ, *then the distribution function* F_n *of*

$$x_n = n^{-\frac{1}{2}} \sum_{v=1}^{n} \xi_v$$

tends to the normal $(0, \sigma)$ *distribution as* n *tends to* ∞.

The characteristic function of x_n is

$$\phi_n(t) = [\phi(tn^{-\frac{1}{2}})]^n, \text{ where}$$

$$\phi(t) = 1 - \tfrac{1}{2}t^2\sigma^2 + \int [e^{itx} - 1 - itx + \tfrac{1}{2}t^2x^2]dF.$$

It follows from the elementary inequality

$$\left| e^{iu} - 1 - iu + \tfrac{1}{2}u^2 \right| \leq \min (u^2, u^3)$$

for real u, that $\left| (e^{itx} - 1 - itx + \tfrac{1}{2}t^2x^2)/t^2 \right|$ is less than x^2 for all t and tends to 0, for every x, as $t \to 0$. It then follows from Lebesgue's convergence theorem that

$$\phi_n(t) = [1 - \tfrac{1}{2}t^2\sigma^2/n + o(t^2/n)]^n \to e^{-\frac{1}{2}t^2\sigma^2},$$

as we require.

In each of the last three theorems, the random variable x_n can be regarded as the sum of a large number of small independent components, and the conclusion in each case is that the distribution function F_n of x_n approximates to one of the three forms—singular, Poisson, normal. The problem of generalising these results and bringing them into a comprehensive theory constitutes the **central limit problem**, and the rest of this section is devoted to the formulation and solution of it.

We use the same notation throughout, and suppose that $x_n = \sum_v x_{nv}$ is a finite sum of independent real numbers x_{nv} and that $F_n(x)$, $F_{nv}(x)$, $\phi_n(t)$, $\phi_{nv}(t)$ are their associated distribution and characteristic functions. The general problem is then to determine the conditions under which F_n tends to some limiting distribution F when the separate components x_{nv} are small (in a sense to be defined more precisely) and to characterise the class of limit distributions F which can arise in this way. The problem is an old and famous one, going back to Bernoulli and Poisson. The solution given here is based on comparatively recent work of Kolmogoroff, Khintchine and Lévy and is highly satisfactory in that it gives a complete characterisation of the class of functions F and gives best possible conditions for convergence.

First, we have to define the sense in which the components x_{nv} are small. We say that x_{nv} are **uniformly small** (with respect to v) as $n \to \infty$ if, for every positive η,

$$\lim_{n \to \infty} \sup_v P\{|x_{nv}| > \eta\} = 0.$$

Before going on to give alternative and equivalent forms of this condition, it is convenient to introduce the notion of the **quasi-mean** of a small variable, which always exists and may be used in place of the mean when this is not defined. We say that a is a quasi-mean of the variable with distribution function $F(x)$ if

$$\int \frac{x}{1+x^2} \, dF(x+a) = 0.$$

It is easy to show that $\int \dfrac{x}{1+x^2} \, dF(x+t)$ decreases strictly and changes sign in the interval $-\frac{1}{4} \leq t \leq \frac{1}{4}$ provided that $F(\frac{1}{4}) - F(-\frac{1}{4}) > \frac{3}{4}$, and a *unique* quasi-mean is therefore defined in $-\frac{1}{4} \leq t \leq \frac{1}{4}$ for such a variable. The next theorem shows that a small variable always has a small quasi-mean, which is therefore uniquely defined. Moreover, the quasi-means of uniformly small variables x_{nv} are all uniquely defined for sufficiently large n. The main facts that we need about uniformly small variables are contained in the following theorem.

THEOREM 7. *Each of the following conditions is equivalent to the condition that x_{nv} are uniformly small.*

(i) $\int_{|x| \geq \eta} dF_{nv} \to 0$ *uniformly in v, for every fixed positive η,*

(ii) $\sup_v |\phi_{nv}(t) - 1| \to 0$ *for each real t as $n \to \infty$,*

(iii) $\phi_{nv}(t) \to 1$ *uniformly in v and t in any finite t-interval, as $n \to \infty$.*

If $\chi(x)$ is continuous and bounded in $-\infty < x < \infty$ and $\chi(x) \geq 0$, $\chi(0) = 0$, and if x_{nv} and constants b_{nv} are uniformly small, then so are $\int \chi(x) dF_{nv}(x + b_{nv})$. In particular, the quasi-means a_{nv} are uniformly small and so are $\int \chi(x) dF_{nv}(x + a_{nv})$.

Condition (i) is plainly equivalent to the defining property. Condition (iii) is as strong as (ii) and can be deduced from (i) by using the elementary inequalities $|1 - e^{ixt}| \leq \min [|xt|, 2]$, so that

$$|\phi_{nv}(t) - 1| = \left| \int (e^{itx} - 1) dF_{nv} \right| \leq \eta(t) + 2 \int_{|x| \geq \eta} dF_{nv}.$$

On the other hand, if we assume (ii), we deduce from Theorem 16 of Section 11 that

$$F_{nv}(\eta) - F_{nv}(-\eta) \geqq \frac{1}{\eta} \int_0^\eta [F_{nv}(x) - F_{nv}(-x)]dx$$

$$= \frac{1}{\pi\eta} \int \frac{1-\cos \eta t}{t^2} \phi_{nv}(t)dt = \frac{1}{\pi\eta} \int \frac{1-\cos \eta t}{t^2} dt - o(1) = 1 - o(1)$$

uniformly in v as $n \to \infty$, and this gives (i).

The next part of the theorem comes from the inequality

$$\int \chi(x)dF_{nv}(x+b_{nv}) \leqq \sup_{|x| \leqq \eta + |b_{nv}|} |\chi(x)| + \int_{|x| > \eta} dF_{nv}$$

for every positive η, and the uniform smallness of a_{nv} from the inequalities

$$0 = \left| \int \frac{x}{1+x^2} dF_{nv}(x+a_{nv}) \right| \geqq \left| \int_{-\varepsilon}^\varepsilon \frac{x-a_{nv}}{1+(x-a_{nv})^2} dF_{n_v} \right| - \tfrac{1}{2}\varepsilon$$

$$\geqq \tfrac{1}{2}[|a_{nv}| - \varepsilon](1-\varepsilon) - \tfrac{1}{2}\varepsilon$$

$$\geqq \tfrac{1}{2}|a_{nv}| - \varepsilon$$

when $0 < \varepsilon \leqq \tfrac{1}{2}$ and n is large enough to ensure that $\int_{|x| \geqq \varepsilon} dF_{nv} \leqq \varepsilon$ and $|a_{nv}| \leqq \tfrac{1}{2}$ for all v.

The general approach to the central limit problem depends on a class of functions introduced by Khintchine and Lévy which extends an earlier one defined for distributions of finite variance introduced by Kolmogoroff. We say that $\psi(t)$ is a **K-L function** with representation (a, G) if

$$\psi(t) = ita + \int \left\{ e^{itx} - 1 - \frac{itx}{1+x^2} \right\} \frac{1+x^2}{x^2} dG,$$

where a is a real number and $G(x)$ is bounded and non-decreasing in $(-\infty, \infty)$. The value of the integrand at $x = 0$ is defined to be $-\tfrac{1}{2}t^2$ and it is then continuous and bounded in $(-\infty, \infty)$ and therefore integrable with respect to G. We also suppose, as we obviously can, that $G(-\infty) = 0$.

The two preliminary theorems on K-L functions which follow are analogues of Theorems 16, 17 and 18 of Section 11 on the relationship between associated distribution and characteristic functions.

THEOREM 8. *A K-L function $\psi(t)$ is bounded and continuous in every finite interval and defines a, G uniquely except at discontinuity points.*

The first part is obvious. To prove uniqueness, we define

$$\theta(t) = \psi(t) - \tfrac{1}{2} \int_{-1}^{1} \psi(t+u)du = \tfrac{1}{2} \int_{-1}^{1} [\psi(t) - \psi(t+u)]du.$$

Then since $\left(1 - \dfrac{\sin y}{y}\right)\dfrac{(1+y^2)}{y^2}$ and its reciprocal are both bounded, we can write

$$\theta(t) = \tfrac{1}{2} \int_{-1}^{1} du \int \left\{ e^{itx}(1 - e^{iux}) + \frac{iux}{1+x^2} \right\} \frac{1+x^2}{x^2} dG$$

$$= \int e^{itx} \left(1 - \frac{\sin x}{x}\right) \frac{1+x^2}{x^2} dG = \int e^{itx} dT,$$

where

$$T(x) = \int_{-\infty}^{x} \left(1 - \frac{\sin y}{y}\right) \frac{1+y^2}{y^2} dG,$$

and

$$G(x) = \int_{-\infty}^{x} \frac{y^2}{(1 - \sin y/y)(1+y^2)} dT.$$

This completes the proof since $G(x)$ is defined uniquely by $T(x)$, which is defined uniquely by $\theta(t)$ by Theorem 16 of Section 11, and this in turn is defined uniquely by $\psi(t)$. The value of a is clearly determined by ψ and G.

The next theorem is concerned with limits of sequences of K-L functions, and we shall write $G_n \to G$ if $G_n(x) \to G(x)$ at every continuity point of $G(x)$ and also at $\pm\infty$ in the sense that $G_n(-\infty) \to G(-\infty)$, $G_n(+\infty) \to G(+\infty)$.

THEOREM 9. *If ψ_n is a K-L function with representation (a_n, G_n) for $n = 1, 2, \ldots$, and if $a_n \to a$ and $G_n \to G$, and $G(x)$ is non-decreasing and bounded, then $\psi_n(t) \to \psi(t)$ uniformly in every finite interval.*

Conversely, if $\psi_n(t) \to \psi(t)$ for all t and $\psi(t)$ is continuous at 0, then $\psi(t)$ is a K-L function with representation $a = \lim a_n$, $G = \lim G_n$.

The first part is proved easily by the argument of Theorem 17 of Section 11. For the second part, we define $\theta_n(t)$, $T_n(x)$ as in the last theorem. Then

$$\theta_n(t) \to \theta(t) = \psi(t) - \tfrac{1}{2} \int_{-1}^{1} \psi(t+u)du,$$

which is continuous at 0, and it follows from Theorem 18 of Section 11 that there is a non-decreasing bounded function T such that $T_n \to T$. It follows then than $G_n \to G$, where G is defined in terms of T by the formula in the last theorem and is non-decreasing and bounded. It follows easily then that $\psi(t)$ is a K-L function with representation (a, G) with $a = \lim a_n$.

We now come to the two theorems which together characterise the limit distribution function of sums of small and independent variables as those for which $\phi(t) = e^{\psi(t)}$ and $\psi(t)$ is a K-L function.

THEOREM 10.   *If $\psi(t)$ is a K-L function, $\phi(t) = e^{\psi(t)}$ is the characteristic function of a distribution function F, and it is possible to define, for each n, independent random real numbers x_{nv} which are uniformly small as $n \to \infty$ and such that $x_n = \sum\limits_v x_{nv}$ has distribution function F_n and $F_n \to F$.*

Since the integrand in the formula

$$\psi(t) = ita + \int \left\{ e^{itx} - 1 - \frac{itx}{1+x^2} \right\} \frac{1+x^2}{x^2} \, dG$$

is continuous, the integral exists in the Riemann-Stieltjes sense, and it is possible to define $\psi_n(t)$, $\psi_{nv}(t)$ so that

$$\psi_n(t) = \sum_v \psi_{nv}(t), \quad \psi_{nv}(t) = c_{nv} \left\{ e^{it\lambda_{nv}} - 1 - \frac{it\lambda_{nv}}{1+\lambda_{nv}^2} \right\}$$

and $\psi_n(t) \to \psi(t)$ for every t. Then $\phi_n(t) = e^{\psi_n(t)} \to \phi(t)$, and since $\phi(t)$ is continuous at 0, it follows from Theorem 18 of Section 11 that it is the characteristic function of a distribution function F and $F_n \to F$. The components x_{nv} are uniformly small if c_{nv} are all small, and it is easy to see that they can be so defined when $G(x)$ is continuous. If $G(x)$ has a discontinuity at λ, say, we have to allow $\lambda_{nv} = \lambda$ for several values of v so that each of the corresponding values c_{nv} is sufficiently small while their sum is the discontinuity in G.

It is plain from the form of $\psi_n(t)$ that the components x_{nv} are all linear functions of variables with Poisson distributions, but this arises from the particular way in which the sequences x_n, x_{nv} are constructed. This can be done in many alternative ways, and the components need not in general be Poisson variables.   In fact, they need not even have finite means, and as it is very desirable not to exclude such components, we use the quasi mean in cases where the mean is not assumed to exist. If the mean does exist in the usual sense, it need not be equal to the quasi-mean, but we shall be concerned only with small variables and the discrepancy is generally of no importance.

THEOREM 11 (*The central limit theorem*).   *Suppose that x_{nv} are independent random real numbers for each n and are uniformly small as $n \to \infty$. Suppose that $x_n = \sum x_{nv}$ has distribution function F_n and that $F_n \to F$ and $\phi(t) \neq 0$. Then the characteristic function of F has the form*

$\phi(t) = e^{\psi(t)}$, where $\psi(t)$ is a K-L function with representation (a, G) given uniquely by $G = \lim G_n$, $a = \lim a_n$,

$$G_n(x) = \sum_v \int_{-\infty}^x \frac{y^2}{1+y^2}\, dF_{nv}(y+a_{nv}), \quad a_n = \sum_v a_{nv}, \tag{1}$$

and F_{nv} is the distribution function of x_{nv} and a_{nv} its quasi-mean.

Conversely, if $\phi(t)$ has the form $e^{\psi(t)}$ and equations (1) hold, then $F_n \to F$.

By the definition of a_{nv}, we have

$$e^{-ita_{nv}}\phi_{nv}(t) = \int e^{itx}dF_{nv}(x+a_{nv}) = 1+\gamma_{nv}(t),$$

where

$$\gamma_{nv}(t) = \int \left\{ e^{itx} - 1 - \frac{itx}{1+x^2} \right\} dF_{nv}(x+a_{nv}), \tag{2}$$

and

$$\alpha_{nv}(t) = -\mathcal{R}\{\gamma_{nv}(t)\} = \int (1-\cos\, tx)dF_{nv}(x+a_{nv}) \geqq 0. \tag{3}$$

Since $e^{itx}-1-itx/(1+x^2)$ is bounded and continuous and vanishes at $x = 0$, it follows from Theorem 7 that $a_{nv} \to 0$ uniformly in v as $n \to \infty$ and that $\gamma_{nv}(t) \to 0$ uniformly in v and t in any fixed interval $|t| \leqq H$. Hence $\phi_{nv}(t)$ will be near to 1 when n is sufficiently large and we can express the principal value of its logarithm in the form

$$\log \phi_{nv}(t) = ita_{nv} + \gamma_{nv}(t) + O\{|\gamma_{nv}(t)|^2\},$$

uniformly in v. It follows then that

$$\phi_n(t) = \prod_v \phi_{nv}(t) = \exp\left\{ ita_n + \sum_v \gamma_{nv}(t) + O\left[\sum_v |\gamma_{nv}(t)|^2 \right] \right\} \tag{4}$$

uniformly in $|t| \leqq H$. Now let

$$A_{nv} = \frac{1}{2H} \int_{-H}^{H} \alpha_{nv}(t)dt = \int \left(1 - \frac{\sin Hx}{Hx} \right) dF_{nv}(x+a_{nv}). \tag{5}$$

It is easy to see that

$$\left| e^{itx} - 1 - \frac{itx}{1+x^2} \right| \leqq C\left(1 - \frac{\sin Hx}{Hx} \right)$$

for $|t| \leqq H$ and all x, where C depends only on H, and it then follows from (2) and (5) that $|\gamma_{nv}(t)| \leqq CA_{nv}$.

If we now equate the moduli of the two sides of (4) and remember that $\alpha_{nv} = -\mathscr{R}\{\gamma_{nv}\}$ and $\sup_{v} |\gamma_{nv}(t)| \to 0$ uniformly in $|t| \leq H$ as $n \to \infty$, we have

$$\sum_{v} \alpha_{nv}(t) \leq -\log |\phi_n(t)| + o\left\{\sum_{v} A_{nv}\right\}$$

uniformly in $|t| \leq H$. After integrating over $(-H, H)$, we get

$$\sum_{v} A_{nv} \leq -\frac{1}{2H} \int_{-H}^{H} \log |\phi_n(t)| \, dt + o\left\{\sum_{v} A_{nv}\right\}. \tag{6}$$

We are given that $\phi_n(t) \to \phi(t)$, and it follows that $\log |\phi_n(t)|$ is uniformly bounded in $|t| \leq H$ for sufficiently large n. Hence $\sum_{v} A_{nv}$ is bounded, and we deduce from (4) and (6) that $\phi_n(t) = e^{\psi_n(t) + o(1)}$ uniformly for $|t| \leq H$, and

$$\psi_n(t) = ita_n + \sum_{v} \gamma_{nv}(t) = ita_n + \int \left\{e^{itx} - 1 - \frac{itx}{1+x^2}\right\} \frac{1+x^2}{x^2} \, dG_n. \tag{7}$$

But $\phi(t) \neq 0$, and we can therefore define a continuous function $\psi(t)$ with $\psi(0) = 0$ so that $\phi(t) = e^{\psi(t)}$. The assumption $F_n \to F$ implies that $\phi_n(t) \to \phi(t)$ uniformly in $|t| \leq H$, and we deduce therefore that $e^{\psi_n(t) - \psi(t)} \to 1$ uniformly in $|t| \leq H$. This is true for *continuous* functions $\psi_n(t)$, $\psi(t)$ only if $\psi_n(t) \to \psi(t)$, and since H can be as large as we please, the conclusion follows from Theorem 9.

For the converse, we use the inequality

$$\left| e^{itx} - 1 - \frac{itx}{1+x^2} \right| \leq C(t) \frac{x^2}{1+x^2},$$

where $G(t)$ is bounded in every finite interval, and deduce from (1) and the fact that $G_n(\infty) \to G(\infty)$ that $\sum_{v} |\gamma_{nv}(t)| \leq C(t)G_n(\infty)$, which is bounded. But $\gamma_{nv}(t) \to 0$ uniformly in v for any fixed t, (4) and (7) remain true, and therefore $\phi_n(t) \to e^{\psi(t)}$, as we require.

The class of limit distributions of the form $\phi(t) = e^{\psi(t)}$ with a *K-L* function $\psi(t)$ plainly contains the singular, normal and Poisson distributions, and we can deduce immediately from Theorem 12 the conditions under which sequences F_n tend to these forms.

THEOREM 12 (*The law of large numbers*). *In order that F_n should tend to the singular form D_c, it is necessary and sufficient that*

$$a_n \to a = c, \quad G_n(x) \to G(x) = 0.$$

THEOREM 13. *In order that F_n should tend to the Poisson distribution with mean c, it is necessary and sufficient that*

$$a_n \to a = \tfrac{1}{2}c, \quad G_n \to G = \frac{c}{2}D(x-1).$$

G

THEOREM 14. *In order that F_n should tend to the normal (m, σ) distribution, it is necessary and sufficient that $a_n \to a = m$, $G_n \to G = \sigma^2 D$.*

The next theorem is of some practical interest in that it gives conditions under which the random variables considered in Theorem 11 have finite means, and shows how these can be used in place of the quasi-means.

THEOREM 15. *Suppose that the conditions of Theorem 11 hold and also that, for every positive u,*

$$\lim_{n \to \infty} \sum_v \int_{|x| \ge u} |x| \, dF_{nv} \le \varepsilon(u), \quad \lim_{u \to 0} \varepsilon(u) = 0. \tag{1}$$

Then $\int |x| \, dG$ exists and the limit distribution F has finite mean m and

$$m = a + \int x \, dG = \lim m_n, \quad m_n = E\{x_n\} = \sum_v m_{nv}, \quad m_{nv} = E\{x_{nv}\}.$$

Moreover, the function G remains unchanged if we replace a_{nv} by m_{nv} in the equation (1), and we can also write

$$\psi(t) = itm + \int \{e^{itx} - 1 - itx\} \frac{1+x^2}{x^2} \, dG. \tag{2}$$

The means $m_{nv} = E\{x_{nv}\}$ can be defined directly by $m_{nv} = \int x \, dF_{nv}$, and by the definition of a_{nv}, we have

$$0 = \int \frac{x}{1+x^2} \, dF_{nv}(x + a_{nv}) = \int (x - a_{nv}) dF_{nv} - \int \frac{x^3}{1+x^2} \, dF_{nv}(x + a_{nv}),$$

and therefore

$$\delta_{nv} = m_{nv} - a_{nv} = \int \frac{x^3}{1+x^2} \, dF_{nv}(x + a_{nv}). \tag{3}$$

Summing over v, we get

$$m_n - a_n = \sum_v \int \frac{x^3}{1+x^2} \, dF_{nv}(x + a_{nv}) = \int x \, dG_n$$

by the definition of G_n. If $u > 1$ and u, $-u$ are points of continuity of G_n for every n, we have

$$\int_{|x| \ge u} |x| \, dG_n = \sum_v \int_{|x| \ge u} \frac{|x| x^2}{1+x^2} \, dF_{nv}(x + a_{nv})$$

$$\le \sum_v \int_{|x - a_{nv}| \ge u} |x - a_{nv}| \, dF_{nv}$$

$$\le \frac{u+1}{u} \sum_v \int_{|x| \ge u-1} |x| \, dF_{nv}$$

$$\le \frac{u+1}{u} \varepsilon(u-1) \tag{4}$$

by (1). Also, if $w > u > 1$,

$$\int_{|x| < w} |x| \, dG = |w| [G(w) - G(-w)] - \int_0^w [G(x) - G(-x)] \, dx$$

$$= \lim_{n \to \infty} \left\{ |w| [G_n(w) - G_n(-w)] - \int_0^w [G_n(x) - G_n(-x)] \, dx \right\}$$

$$= \lim_{n \to \infty} \int_{|x| < w} |x| \, dG_n$$

$$\leq \lim_{n \to \infty} \left\{ u \int_{|x| < u} dG_n + \int_{|x| \geq u} |x| \, dG_n \right\}$$

$$\leq u G(\infty) + \frac{u+1}{u} \varepsilon(u-1)$$

by (4) and the fact that $\int dG_n = G_n(\infty) \to G(\infty)$. This shows that $\int |x| \, dG$ exists, and a similar argument to that used above shows that

$$\int_{|x| < u} x \, dG_n \to \int_{|x| < u} x \, dG.$$

Hence, if $u > 1$,

$$\lim_{n \to \infty} \left| \int x \, dG - \int x \, dG_n \right| \leq \int_{|x| \geq u} |x| \, dG + \int_{|x| \geq u} |x| \, dG_n$$

$$+ \lim_{n \to \infty} \left| \int_{|x| < u} x \, dG - \int_{|x| < u} x \, dG_n \right|$$

$$\leq \int_{|x| \geq u} |x| \, dG + \frac{u+1}{u} \varepsilon(u-1),$$

which can be made as small as we please by choice of u. Since $a_n \to a$, by Theorem 11, it follows that

$$m = \lim_{n \to \infty} m_n = a + \int x \, dG,$$

and the formula (2) then follows from the fact that

$$\int \left\{ itx - \frac{itx}{1+x^2} \right\} \frac{1+x^2}{x^2} \, dG = it \int x \, dG = it(m-a).$$

Finally, to show that m_{nv} can be substituted for a_{nv} in equations (1) of Theorem 11, we have

$$\left| \sum_v \int_{-\infty}^x \frac{y^2}{1+y^2} \, dF_{nv}(y+m_{nv}) - \sum_v \int_{-\infty}^x \frac{y^2}{1+y^2} \, dF_{nv}(y+a_{nv}) \right|$$

$$= \left| \sum_v \int_{-\infty}^x \frac{\delta_{nv}(2y+\delta_{nv})}{(1+y^2)\{1+(y+\delta_{nv})^2\}} \, dF_{nv}(y+a_{nv}) \right|$$

$$\leq \sum_v \delta_{nv}^2 + 2 \sum_v |\delta_{nv}| \int \frac{|y|}{1+y^2} \, dF_{nv}(y+a_{nv})$$

$$= o \left\{ \sum_v |\delta_{nv}| \right\} \quad \text{as } n \to \infty \tag{5}$$

since

$$|\delta_{nv}| \leq \int \frac{|x|^3}{1+x^2} \, dF_n(x+a_{nv})$$

by (3). This last expression and

$$\int \frac{|y|}{1+y^2} \, dF_{nv}(y+a_{nv})$$

are both uniformly small by Theorem 7 and our assumptions about F_{nv}. Also,

$$\sum_v |\delta_{nv}| \leq \sum_v \int \frac{|x|^3}{1+x^2} \, dF_n(x+a_{nv}) = \int |x| \, dG_n,$$

which is bounded, and this with (5) completes the proof.

The following important special case is an immediate corollary.

THEOREM 16. *The conclusions of Theorem 15 hold if, instead of* (1), *we assume that* x_{nv} *have finite standard deviations* σ_{nv} *and that* $\sigma_n^2 = \sum_v \sigma_{nv}^2$ *is bounded.*

This gives the following simple, but weaker, form of Theorem 14.

THEOREM 17 (*Liapounoff*). *If* x_{nv} *has mean* 0 *and standard deviation* σ_{nv}, *and if* $\Sigma \, \sigma_{nv}^2 = 1$, *a necessary and sufficient condition that* F_n *should tend to the normal* (0, 1) *distribution is that, for every* $\eta > 0$,

$$L(\eta) = \sum_v \int_{|x| \geq \eta} x^2 \, dF_{nv} \to 0 \quad \text{as } n \to \infty. \tag{1}$$

The condition $\Sigma \, \sigma_{nv}^2 = 1$ means that

$$\sum_v \int_{|x| < \eta} x^2 \, dF_{nv} = \sum_v \int x^2 \, dF_{nv} - \sum_v \int_{|x| \geq \eta} x^2 \, dF_{nv} = 1 - L(\eta),$$

and the equivalence of (1) and the condition $G_n \to D$ is apparent from the inequalities

$$\frac{1-L(\eta)}{1+\eta^2} \leqq \int_{|x|<\eta} dG \leqq 1-L(\eta), \quad \int_{|x|\geqq\eta} dG \leqq L(\eta).$$

The limit distribution and characteristic functions which have been investigated in this section can be characterised in a different way. We say that a characteristic function $\phi(t)$ (or its associated distribution function or random variable) is **infinitely divisible** if, for every positive integer n, we can write $\phi(t) = [\phi_n(t)]^n$, where $\phi_n(t)$ is a characteristic function. We deduce immediately from Theorem 11.

THEOREM 18.   *A characteristic function $\phi(t)$ is infinitely divisible if and only if it can be expressed in the form $\phi(t) = e^{\psi(t)}$, where $\psi(t)$ is a K-L function.*

An important class of infinitely divisible distribution functions arises from the consideration of **cumulative sums**

$$x_n = \frac{\xi_1 + \xi_2 + \dots \xi_n}{\lambda_n},$$

where $\xi_1, \xi_2, \dots, \xi_n$ are independent and $\lambda_n > 0$. The limit of the distribution of x_n is infinitely divisible if the components $\xi_v \lambda_n^{-1}$ are uniformly small, and the following theorem gives conditions for this.

THEOREM 19.   *If x_n is a cumulative sum and its components $\xi_v \lambda_n^{-1}$ are uniformly small and if $\phi_n(t) \to \phi(t)$, where $\phi(t)$ is a non-singular characteristic function, then $\lambda_n \to \infty$, $\lambda_{n+1}/\lambda_n \to 1$.*

The first conclusion is obvious. For the second, we have

$$x_{n+1} = \frac{\lambda_n x_n}{\lambda_{n+1}} + \frac{\xi_{n+1}}{\lambda_{n+1}},$$

and since the last term is small in probability as $n \to \infty$, it follows that $F(\lambda_{n+1}x/\lambda_n)$ and $F_n(x)$ have the same limit distribution function $F(x)$. But if lim sup $\lambda_n/\lambda_{n+1} \geqq \theta$, we have $F_n(\lambda_{n+1}x/\lambda_n) \geqq F_n(\theta x)$ for infinitely many n, and therefore $F(x) \geqq F(\theta x)$ for all x. This implies that $\theta \leqq 1$, and a similar argument shows that lim inf $\lambda_n/\lambda_{n+1} \geqq 1$.

We call the limit function of a sequence of cumulative sums of uniformly small variable a **cumulative distribution**, and it is clear that any such distribution is infinitely divisible. The converse is not true, as the class of cumulative distributions is a proper subclass of the class of infinitely divisible distributions. The following theorem shows how the subclass can be characterised by a property of $\phi(t)$.

A characteristic function $\phi(t)$ is called **self-decomposable** if, for every c in $0 < c < 1$, it is possible to write $\phi(t) = \phi(ct)\phi_c(t)$ where $\phi_c(t)$ is also a characteristic function.

THEOREM 20 (*P. Lévy*). *A distribution with characteristic function* $\phi(t)$ *is cumulative if and only if it is self-decomposable; and* $\phi_c(t)$ *is then also infinitely divisible.*

We suppose that $\phi(t)$ is self-decomposable and prove first that $\phi(t) \neq 0$. Otherwise, if $\phi(t)$ has a positive zero, it has a least, since $\phi(0) = 1$ and $\phi(t)$ is continuous, and we denote this zero by a. Then $\phi(2ac) \neq 0$ if $0 < c < 1$, and since $\phi(2a) = \phi(2ac)\phi_c(2a)$, it follows that $\phi_c(2a) = 0$. Hence

$$1 = 1 - \mathscr{R}\{\phi_c(2a)\} = \int (1 - \cos 2ax)dF_c$$
$$= 2 \int (1 - \cos ax)(1 + \cos ax)dF_c \leq 4 \int (1 - \cos ax)dF_c$$
$$= 4[1 - \mathscr{R}\{\phi_c(a)\}] = 4[1 - \mathscr{R}\{\phi(a)/\phi(ac)\}].$$

This is impossible when c is near enough to 1, since $\phi(ac) \rightarrow \phi(a)$, and it follows that $\phi(t) \neq 0$ for $t \geq 0$, and by a similar argument for $t \leq 0$.

It follows from our hypothesis that $\beta_1(t) = \phi(t)$,

$$\beta_v(t) = \phi_{(v-1)/v}(vt) = \phi(vt)/\phi[(v-1)t], \quad (v = 2, 3, \ldots, n)$$

are characteristic functions, and the decomposition

$$\phi(t) = \phi_n(t) = \prod_{v=1}^{n} \beta_v(t/n)$$

shows that $\phi(t)$ is the limit of characteristic function of cumulative sums with $\lambda_n = n$.

Conversely, if $\phi(t)$ is cumulative, we have $\phi(t) = \lim \phi_n(t)$, where

$$\phi_n(t) = \prod_{v=1}^{n} \beta_v(t\lambda_n),$$

$$\phi_{n+m}(t) = \phi_n(\lambda_n t/\lambda_{n+m})\chi_{n, m}(t),$$

and

$$\chi_{n, m}(t) = \prod_{v=n+1}^{n+m} \beta_v(t/\lambda_{n+m})$$

is a characteristic function. If $0 < c < 1$, we can use Theorem 16 to define $m = m(n)$ so that $\lambda_n/\lambda_{n+m} \rightarrow c$, and then

$$\phi_{n+m}(t) \rightarrow \phi(t), \quad \phi_n(\lambda_n t/\lambda_{n+m}) \rightarrow \phi(ct),$$

since $\phi_n(t) \rightarrow \phi(t)$ uniformly in any finite interval. But $\phi(t)$ is infinitely divisible and does not vanish and $\chi_{n, m}(t)$ converges for every t to the function $\phi_c(t) = \phi(t)/\phi(ct)$ which is continuous at $t = 0$ and therefore a characteristic function by Theorem 18 of Section 11. Moreover, the form of $\chi_{n,\,m}(t)$ shows that $\phi_c(t)$ is infinitely divisible.

The following theorem shows that the cumulative distributions can also be characterised by their $K\text{-}L$ representations $G(x)$.

THEOREM 21. *In order that an infinitely divisible distribution should be cumulative it is necessary and sufficient that the functions*

$$-\int_u^\infty (1+e^{-2v})dG(e^v), \qquad -\int_{-\infty}^u (1+e^{-2v})dG(-e^v)$$

should be convex in $-\infty < u < \infty$.

We suppose that $\phi(t)$ is cumulative and therefore self decomposable. If $0 < c < 1$, it then follows that the $K\text{-}L$ representation $G_c(x)$ of $\phi_c(t)$ is given for $x > 0$ by

$$\int_x^\infty \frac{1+y^2}{y^2}\, dG_c = Q(x/c) - Q(x),$$

$$Q(x) = -\int_{-x}^\infty \frac{1+y^2}{y^2}\, dG.$$

Since $\phi_c(t)$ is infinitely divisible, $G_c(y)$ must increase, and this means that $Q(x/c) - Q(x)$ decreases in $x > 0$ for every value of c in $0 < c < 1$. If $q(u) = Q(e^u)$, this means that $q(u+d) - q(u)$ decreases in $-\infty < u < \infty$ for every positive d, and $q(u)$ is therefore convex. A similar argument applies in the range $x < 0$, and the converse part is trivial.

COROLLARY. *If $G(x)$ is the $K\text{-}L$ representation of a cumulative infinitely divisible distribution, then $G(x)$ is continuous except possibly at $x = 0$, it is differentiable except in at most a countable set of points and $(x^2 + 1)G'(x)/x$ decreases outside this set.*

This follows from familiar properties † of convex functions.

The class of cumulative distributions can be specialised further by the condition that the component random variable should be identically distributed, and again there is a characterisation of this subclass by a property of $\phi(t)$. We say that a characteristic function $\phi(t)$ is **stable** if, for every positive constant b,

$$\phi(t)\phi(bt) = e^{ia't}\phi(b't)$$

for some constant a' and a positive constant b' (both depending on b). This means that the sum of two linear functions of independent random variables with the same stable distribution is also a linear function of a variable of the same type.

† HARDY, LITTLEWOOD and POLYA, *Inequalities*, Cambridge, 1934, page 91.

THEOREM 22. *A distribution with characteristic function $\phi(t)$ is stable if and only if it is infinitely divisible and $\phi(t) = e^{\psi(t)}$, where either*

$$\psi(t) = ita - A|t|^{\alpha}\left\{1 + \frac{it\theta}{|t|}\tan\frac{\pi\alpha}{2}\right\},$$

$$A > 0, \quad -1 \leq \theta \leq 1, \quad 0 < |\alpha - 1| < 1,$$

or

$$\psi(t) = ita - A|t|\left\{1 + \frac{2it\theta}{\pi|t|}\log|t|\right\}.$$

If we assume that $\phi(t)$ is stable, we can define $\lambda_n > 0$ and a_n, for $n = 1, 2, \ldots$ so that $[\phi(t)]^n = e^{ita_n}\phi(\lambda_n t)$ and then

$$\phi(t) = \{\phi(t/\lambda_n)e^{-ita_n/n\lambda_n}\}^n.$$

The distribution is therefore infinitely divisible and $\phi(t) = e^{\psi(t)}$ with a *K-L* representation (a_0, G) for $\psi(t)$. Now let

$$Q(x) = \int_{-\infty}^{x} \frac{1+y^2}{y^2}\,dG, \quad (-\infty < x < 0),$$

$$Q(x) = -\int_{x}^{\infty} \frac{1+y^2}{y^2}\,dG, \quad (0 < x < \infty),$$

so that

$$\psi(t) = ita_0 + \int\left\{e^{itx} - 1 - \frac{itx}{1+x^2}\right\}dQ$$

and the stability condition takes the form

$$\psi(t) + \psi(bt) = ita' + \psi(b't).$$

It follows from Theorem 8 and the condition $Q(-\infty) = Q(\infty) = 0$ that

$$Q(x) + Q(x/b) = Q(x/b'),$$

and if we consider first the range $x > 0$ and let $x = e^u$, $q(u) = Q(e^u)$, $d = \log b$, $d' = \log b'$, we get $q(u) + q(u-d) = q(u-d')$. This has the general solution $q(u) = -Ae^{-\alpha u}$, where α is a real or complex number satisfying $1 + b^\alpha = b'^\alpha$, and therefore $Q(x) = -A_1 x^{-\alpha}$. Since $G(x)$ is real, increasing and bounded, this implies that α is real, $0 < \alpha < 2$ and $A_1 > 0$. A similar argument can be applied in the range $-\infty < x < 0$ with the same values of b and b', and since α is defined uniquely by b, b', it follows that $Q(x) = A_2|x|^{-\alpha}$, $A_2 > 0$ in $-\infty < x < 0$. After substituting this form for $Q(x)$ in the formula for $\psi(t)$, we use the following identities, which can be established easily for real t by contour integration:

$$\int_0^\infty \left\{ e^{itx} - 1 - \frac{itx}{1+x^2} \right\} x^{-\alpha-1} dx = (-it)^\alpha \Gamma(-\alpha) + ita,$$

$$(0 < \alpha < 1 \text{ and } 1 < \alpha < 2),$$

$$\int_0^\infty \left\{ e^{itx} - 1 - \frac{itx}{1+x^2} \right\} x^{-2} dx = -\tfrac{1}{2}\pi |t| - it \log |t| + ita_2,$$

where a_1, a_2 are real and depend only on α. The conclusion follows with $\theta = (A_1 - A_2)/(A_1 + A_2)$ and

$$A = -(A_1 + A_2)\alpha \cos (\tfrac{1}{2}\alpha\pi)\Gamma(-\alpha), \quad (\alpha \neq 1),$$

$$A = \tfrac{1}{2}\pi(A_1 + A_2) \qquad\qquad , \quad (\alpha = 1).$$

Conversely, it is easy to show that $\phi(t)$ is stable when $\psi(t)$ takes either of the two special forms. As an immediate corollary, we have.

THEOREM 23.   *The only symmetrical stable distributions are given by* $\phi(t) = e^{-A|x|^\alpha}$ *with* $0 < \alpha < 2$. *Case* $\alpha = 2$ *gives the normal distribution,* $\alpha = 1$ *gives the Cauchy distribution.*

THEOREM 24.   *A distribution is the limit of cumulative sums of uniformly small and identically distributed random variables if and only if it is stable and* $a' = 0$. *A necessary and sufficient condition for this, in the notation of Theorem* 20, *is that* $\alpha \neq 0$, $a = 0$, *or* $\alpha = 1$, $\theta = 0$.

If we suppose that the distribution is stable and $a' = 0$, the stability condition is $\phi(t)\phi(bt) = \phi(b't)$, and we can define positive numbers λ_n for every n so that $[\phi(t)]^n = \phi(\lambda_n t)$, $\phi(t) = [\phi(t/\lambda_n)]^n$, and $\phi(t)$ is therefore the characteristic function of the sum $\lambda_n^{-1}\Sigma\xi_v$, where ξ_v are independent and all have the characteristic function $\phi(t)$.

For the converse, we assume that a characteristic function χ and a sequence of positive numbers λ_n can be defined so that $\lambda_n \to \infty, \lambda_{n+1}/\lambda_n \to 1$,

$$\phi_n(t) = [\chi(t/\lambda_n)]^n \to \phi(t).$$

If $0 < b < 1$, we define $r = r(n)$ so that $\lambda_r/\lambda_n \to b$. Then

$$[\phi_n(t)]^{r/n} = [\chi(t/\lambda_n)]^r = \phi_r(\lambda_r t/\lambda_n).$$

Since $\phi_n(t) \to \phi(t)$ uniformly in any finite interval by Theorem 17 of Section 11, $\phi_r(\lambda_r t/\lambda_n) \to \phi(bt)$, and therefore $[\phi_n(t)]^{r/n} \to \phi(bt)$ for all real t. If we choose a value of t for which $\phi(t) \neq 1$, this implies that r/n tends to a limit g with $0 \leq g \leq 1$ and that $\phi(bt) = [\phi(t)]^g$. Moreover, $0 < g < 1$ unless $\phi(t)$ is singular, and since the distribution is infinitely divisible we have $\phi(t) = e^{\psi(t)}$, $\psi(bt) = g\psi(t)$. It follows from these equations, put in terms of $G(x)$, that $G(x)$ has the same form as for the stable distributions of Theorem 20. It is also easy to verify that the condition $\psi(bt) = g\psi(t)$ also implies that $a = 0$ if $\alpha \neq 1$ and $\theta = 0$ if $\alpha = 1$ and that $g = b^\alpha$ in both cases.

§ 18 RANDOM SEQUENCES AND FUNCTIONS

We have seen in Section 15 that the idea of a random vector $x = (x_1, x_2, ..., x_n)$ can be derived from that of probability measure in $\mathcal{R}_n$. If we think of the vector as a real-valued function defined over a finite set of integers, it is easy to see how the idea of a random sequence or function can be developed. We suppose that $\mathcal{X}$ is the space of all real-valued functions $x(t)$ defined over an arbitrary index space $\mathcal{T}$, and say that $x(t)$ is a **random function** in $\mathcal{X}$ if a probability measure $\mu(X)$ is defined in $\mathcal{X}$ and the statement that $P\{x \in X\} = p$ is interpreted to mean that X is measurable with respect to μ and $\mu(X) = p$. This is quite analogous to the idea of a random real number, and we get a **random n-vector** if $\mathcal{T}$ is a finite space and a **random sequence** if $\mathcal{T}$ is the countable set of positive integers. In the last case, it is usually convenient to use the conventional notation $x = x_1, x_2, ... = \{x_v\}$. Otherwise, there is no need to put any restriction on $\mathcal{T}$, but in the illustrations we consider it will always be a subset of the real line. In many applications it is useful to use t to denote time, and the random function is then called a **random** or **stochastic process** or (particularly when the variable is integral) a **time series**.

The basic problem can now be stated in a form analogous to that associated with the idea of a random variable in its simplest form. It is to establish the existence of a probability measure in $\mathcal{X}$ with certain properties, which usually ensure that a certain specified family of sets are measurable and have specified measures. These specified measures must, of course, be mutually consistent. The specified sets which turn out to be appropriate are the **simple sets** defined as finite unions of **rectangular sets** of functions $x(t)$ satisfying a *finite* set of conditions of the type $a_v \leq x(t_v) < b_v$. It is plain that the simple sets associated with a particular finite system of points t_v form a ring, and that the totality of *all* such simple sets also forms a ring. The basic theorem of Kolmogoroff can be stated in a form closely analogous to Theorem 24 of Section 7.

THEOREM 25 (*Kolmogoroff*). *Suppose that a non-negative additive set function $\mu_0(I)$ is given on the ring of all simple sets I of $\mathcal{X}$ and that for every finite set of points $(t_1, t_2, ..., t_n)$, the values of $\mu_0(I)$ on the ring of sets associated with $t_1, ..., t_n$ are those of a probability distribution in $\mathcal{R}_n$. Then it is possible to define a probability measure $\mu(X)$ in $\mathcal{X}$ in such a way that every simple set I is measurable and $\mu(I) = \mu_0(I)$.*

After Theorem 2 of Section 3 and Theorem 24 of Section 7, it is sufficient to show that if I_n is simple and $I_n{\downarrow}0$, then $\mu(I_n){\to}0$. We suppose the contrary and derive a contradiction. Since the number of values of t associated with any one I_n is finite, the set of all such points t is countable, and they can be arranged as a sequence $\{t_i\}$. Now each I_n is the union of a finite set of rectangular sets and we can select *one* of these for $n = 1, 2, \dots$, so that it contains a *closed* rectangular set J_n with the property that $\lim\limits_{m\to\infty} \mu(J_n I_m) > 0$. Also, we may choose J_n so that $J_{n+1} \subset J_n$, and we have therefore a decreasing sequence of closed non-empty rectangular sets J_n defined by

$$a_{in} \leqq y_i \leqq b_{in} \quad (i = 1, 2, \dots, i_n).$$

For each i there is at least one point y_i which is contained in all the intervals $[a_{in}, b_{in}]$, and any function $x(t)$ for which $x(t_i) = y_i$ for $i = 1, 2, 3, \dots$ belongs to every J_n and so to every I_n. This is impossible since $I_n{\downarrow}0$, and therefore we have $\mu(I_n){\to}0$.

The theorem applies immediately to the definition of random sequences when $\mathscr{T}$ is the space of positive integers. The case in which the terms x_n are independent is of particular interest and can be formulated more simply as follows.

THEOREM 26. *Suppose that F_1, F_2, $\dots$ are distribution functions. Then it is possible to define a probability measure in the space of real sequence x_1, x_2, $\dots$ in such a way that the set of sequences satisfying conditions $a_i \leqq x_{n_i} < b_i$ for any finite set of positive integers n_i is measurable and has measure $\Pi\{F(b_i - 0) - F(a_i - 0)\}$.*

More generally, if μ_v is the probability distribution of x_v (defined by F_v), the set $\mathscr{E}\{x_{n_i} \in X_i\}$ for any finite set of integers n_i and measurable sets X_i of $\mathscr{R}$ is measurable and has measure $\Pi\mu_{n_i}(X_i)$.

The random function defined by this theorem is said to have **independent** terms x_v with distributions F_v. The theorem provides a completely satisfactory basis for the discussion of the probability theory of independent sequences, and their properties of boundedness, convergence, summability and so on which can be expressed in terms of countable sets of conditions. The theorems which follow serve to illustrate some of the methods which may be used. The first is a general result of wide application called the **0 or 1 principle** of Borel.

THEOREM 27. *The probability that a random sequence of independent variables should have a property (e.g. convergence) which is not affected by changes in a finite number of terms is equal to 0 or 1.*

Let X be the set of sequences with the given property, so that our hypothesis is that for every $N \geq 1$, $X = \mathcal{R}_1 \otimes \mathcal{R}_2 \otimes \ldots \mathcal{R}_N \otimes X_N$, where X_N is a set in the space of sequences $(x_{n+1}, x_{n+2}, \ldots)$. If I is any simple set in $\mathcal{X}$, it follows that $I = I \cap X_N$ for large enough N and

$$\mu(I \cap X) = \mu(I)\mu(X_N) = \mu(I)\mu(X).$$

Since this holds for all simple sets, it extends to all measurable sets Y and $\mu(Y \cap X) = \mu(Y)\mu(X)$. In particular, putting $Y = X$,

$$\mu(X) = [\mu(X)]^2, \quad \mu(X) = 0 \text{ or } 1.$$

We can now proceed to discuss some general questions on the convergence of series of independent random real variables. By the last theorem, the series converges with probability 0 or 1. If the value is 1, the sum of the series is a function of x on $\mathcal{X}$ and is therefore itself a random variable. The main problem is to determine how the convergence or divergence of the series is related to the sequence of distribution or characteristic functions of the variables x_v.

The following theorem gives a completely satisfactory answer in one direction.

THEOREM 28. *If* x_1, x_2, ... *are independent random real numbers, and* $s_n = \sum\limits_{v=1}^{n} x_v$ *converges to the (random) sum* s *with probability* 1, *then* $s_n \to s$ *in probability and the distribution and characteristic functions of* s_n *tend to those of* s.

If we think of s_n and s as functions of x over $\mathcal{X}$, and if $\varepsilon > 0$, we have

$$P\{|s_n - s| > \varepsilon\} \leq P\{\sup_{v \geq n} |s_v - s| > \varepsilon\} = \mu(X_n),$$

where μ is the probability distribution of x in $\mathcal{X}$ and X_n is the set of series for which $\sup\limits_{v \geq n} |s_v - s| > \varepsilon$. These sets X_n decrease and tend to the nul set of divergent series, and therefore $\mu(X_n) \to 0$ for every positive ε, and $s_n \to s$ in probability. The second part follows at once from Theorem 1.

The next theorem is the basis of the converse theory in which we deduce convergence with probability 1 from properties of the distribution. It is restricted to series of terms with finite variance, but we shall see later that this is not a serious limitation to the application of the theorem.

THEOREM 29 (*Kolmogoroff's Inequality*). *If* x_v *are independent, with means* 0 *and standard deviations* σ_v, *and if*

$$s_n = \sum_{v=1}^{n} x_v, \quad t_n = \sup_{v \leq n} |s_v|, \quad \varepsilon > 0,$$

then

$$P\{t_n \geq \varepsilon\} \leq \varepsilon^{-2} \sum_{v=1}^{n} \sigma_v^2.$$

The sets $X_v = \mathscr{E}\{|s_v| \geq \varepsilon, t_{v-1} < \varepsilon\}$ are disjoint for $v = 1, 2, \ldots$ and

$$X = \mathscr{E}\{t_n \geq \varepsilon\} = \bigcup_{v=1}^{n} X_v.$$

Moreover, since x_v are independent,

$$\sum_{v=1}^{n} \sigma_v^2 = \int s_n^2 d\mu \geq \int_X s_n^2 d\mu = \sum_{v=1}^{n} \int_{X_v} s_n^2 d\mu$$

$$= \sum_{v=1}^{n} \int_{X_v} (s_v + x_{v+1} + x_{v+2} + \ldots + x_n)^2 d\mu$$

$$= \sum_{v=1}^{n} \int_{X_v} s_v^2 d\mu + \sum_{v=1}^{n-1} \mu(X_v) \sum_{i=v+1}^{n} \sigma_i^2,$$

since X_v is the product of the whole of the space of sequences $(x_{v+1}, x_{v+2}, \ldots)$ and a set of measure $\mu(X_v)$ in the finite dimensional space of $(x_1, x_2, \ldots, x_v)$. Hence

$$\sum_{v=1}^{n} \sigma_v^2 \geq \sum_{v=1}^{n} \int_{X_v} s_v^2 d\mu \geq \varepsilon^2 \sum_{v=1}^{n} \mu(X_v) = \varepsilon^2 \mu(X),$$

as we require.

The simplest form of converse of Theorem 28 follows easily from this.

THEOREM 30. *If x_v are independent with means m_v and standard deviations σ_v, and if $\Sigma \sigma_v^2 < \infty$, then $\Sigma(x_v - m_v)$ converges with probability 1.*

It is obviously sufficient to prove the theorem in the case $m_v = 0$, and then it follows from Theorem 29 applied to variables $x_{m+1}, x_{m+2}, \ldots, x_{m+n}$ that

$$P\{\sup_{1 \leq v \leq n} |s_{m+v} - s_m| > 1/k\} \leq k^2 \sum_{v=m+1}^{m+n} \sigma_v^2,$$

and since $|s_{m+v} - s_{m+q}| > 1/k$ with $1 \leq q \leq v \leq n$ implies that $|s_{m+v} - s_m| > 1/2k$ or $|s_{m+q} - s_m| > 1/2k$, we have

$$P\left\{\sup_{1 \leq q \leq v \leq n} |s_{m+v} - s_{m+q}| > 1/k\right\} \leq 2k^2 \sum_{v=m+1}^{m+n} \sigma_v^2.$$

Therefore

$$P\left\{\lim_{m\to\infty}\ \sup_{1\le q\le v}\ \left|s_{m+v}-s_{m+q}\right|>0\right\}$$

$$=\lim_{k\to\infty}P\left\{\lim_{m\to\infty}\ \sup_{1\le q\le v}\ \left|s_{m+v}-s_{m+q}\right|>1/k\right\}$$

$$=\lim_{k\to\infty}\ \lim_{m\to\infty}\ \lim_{n\to\infty}P\left\{\sup_{1\le q\le v\le n}\ \left|s_{m+v}-s_{m+q}\right|>1/k\right\}$$

$$\le\lim_{m\to\infty}2k^2\sum_{v=m+1}^{\infty}\sigma_v^2$$

$$=0$$

by the convergence of $\Sigma\sigma_v^2$. But $\lim_{m\to\infty}\ \sup_{1\le q\le v}\ \left|s_{m+v}-s_{m+q}\right|>0$ is the necessary and sufficient condition for the divergence of Σx_v, by the general principle of convergence, and the conclusion follows.

It can now be shown that the condition on the standard deviations, or even their existence, need not be assumed in Theorem 30.

THEOREM 31. *Suppose that x_v are independent and have distribution and characteristic functions F_v, ϕ_v. Let $c>0$ and $x_v'=x_v$ or 0 according as $\left|x_v\right|\le c$ or $\left|x_v\right|>c$ and let m_v', σ_v' be the means and standard deviations of x_v' and $p_v'=P\{\left|x_v\right|>c\}$. Then the following conditions are equivalent.* (i) Σx_v *converges with probability* 1, (ii) $\prod_{v=1}^{n}\phi_v$ *converges as $n\to\infty$ to a characteristic function,* (iii) $\Sigma p_v', \Sigma\sigma_v'^2$ *and $\Sigma m_v'$ all converge.*

We have already proved in Theorem 28 that (i) implies (ii). We therefore assume (ii) and follow the argument of Theorem 11 by writing

$$e^{ita_v}\phi_v(t)=\int e^{itx}dF_v(x+a_v)=1+\gamma_v(t),$$

$$A_v=-\tfrac{1}{2}\int_{-1}^{1}\mathscr{R}\{\gamma_v(t)\}dt=\int\left\{1-\frac{\sin x}{x}\right\}dF_v(x+a_v),$$

where a_v is the quasi-mean of x_v. It follows, as in Theorem 11, that Σa_v and

$$\Sigma A_v=\Sigma\int\left\{1-\frac{\sin x}{x}\right\}dF_v(x+a_v)$$

both converge, and since

$$1-\frac{\sin x}{x}\ge\frac{Cx^2}{1+x^2}$$

for all x and some positive C, this shows that

$$\Sigma \int \frac{x^2}{1+x^2} \, dF_v(x+a_v) < \infty. \tag{1}$$

But $\left| a_v \right| \leq \frac{1}{2}c$ for sufficiently large v, and for these values

$$p_v' = \int_{|x|>c} dF_v = \int_{|x+a_v|>c} dF_v(x+a_v) \leq \frac{c^2+4}{c^2} \int \frac{x^2}{1+x^2} \, dF_v(x+a_v),$$

and therefore $\Sigma p_v' < \infty$. Also,

$$\sigma_v'^2 \leq E\{(x_v'-a_v)^2\} = \int_{|x|\leq c} (x-a_v)^2 dF_v$$

$$= \int_{|x+a_v|\leq c} x^2 dF_v(x+a_v) \leq (1+4c^2) \int \frac{x^2}{1+x^2} \, dF_v(x+a_v),$$

where v is large enough to ensure that $\left| a_v \right| \leq c$, and the convergence of $\Sigma \sigma_v'^2$ follows. Using the formulae

$$\int \frac{x}{1+x^2} \, dF_v(x+a_v) = 0, \quad m_v' = \int_{|x+a_v|\leq c} (x+a_v) dF_v(x+a_v),$$

we find that $m_v' - a_v$ has the value

$$\int_{|x+a_v|\leq c} \frac{x^3}{1+x^2} \, dF_v(x+a_v) - \int_{|x+a_v|>c} \left\{ \frac{x}{1+x^2} + a_v \right\} dF_v(x+a_v)$$

and the convergence of $\Sigma(m_v' - a_v)$ follows from (i). Since Σa_v converges, so must $\Sigma m_v'$, and this completes the deduction of (iii).

Finally, to show that (iii) implies (i), we deduce from (iii) and Theorem 30 that $\Sigma(x_v' - m_v)$ converges and so therefore does $\Sigma x_v'$, with probability 1. But

$$P\{x_v' = x_v \text{ for } v \geq n\} = P\{\left| x_v \right| \leq c \text{ for } v \geq n]$$

$$= \prod_{v=n}^{\infty} (1-p_v') = 1 - o(1)$$

as $n \to \infty$, by the convergence of $\Sigma p_v'$ and the consequent convergence of the product. This means that there is probability 1 that $x_v = x_v'$ for sufficiently large v and that Σx_v converges with $\Sigma x_v'$.

The equivalence of (i) and (iii) in Theorem 31 is usually called Kolmogoroff's **three series** theorem and has a simple and useful corollary for bounded variables.

THEOREM 32. *If x_v are independent and bounded, with means m_v and standard deviations σ_v, then Σx_v converges with probability 1 if and only if $\Sigma \sigma_v^2$ and Σm_v both converge.*

We can now proceed a little further in the theory of random functions $x(t)$ defined over the whole real line $\mathcal{T}$. The foundation of the theory is Kolmogoroff's existence theorem which shows that a significant measure can be defined in $\mathcal{X}$ in such a way that all the simple sets are measurable and have any assigned measures, provided that these are mutually consistent. The measure defined in this way over the minimal Borel extension of the simple sets will be called K-**measure** and it is determined and characterised by the totality of all the finite dimensional distributions associated with all finite sets of points in $\mathcal{T}$. In fact, we may call these the finite dimensional **generating distributions** and speak of the K-measure defined by them.

The first major problem in the theory arises from the fact that a K-measure is generally not extensive enough, in that it leaves as unmeasurable many important classes of functions $x(t)$. For example, we find that the class of continuous functions is not measurable with respect to a K-measure. The reason for this is that, unlike the convergence properties discussed in the first part of this section, continuity, differentiability, boundedness and other properties cannot be expressed in terms of a *countable* number of conditions of the kind used in the specification of the simple sets.

In order to deal with these properties, it is therefore necessary to introduce *extensions* of a K-measure. It is generally possible to extend a K-measure in many different ways. Some of the extensions may include or be extensions of others, while some systems of extensions may be mutually inconsistent. But all of them must, of course, be consistent with the K-measure on which they are based.

The general problem is therefore to investigate the system of extensions of a K-measure, to determine whether there is any one of them which make the required sets measurable and, if there are several, to choose the most useful or appropriate one. For example, in many important cases it is possible to extend the same K-measure in two different and mutually inconsistent ways so that, in the first, almost all functions are continuous while, in the second, almost all functions are discontinuous. We should normally choose the first, and the question of the existence of such an extension of a given K-measure is an important problem.

While the definition of random functions in terms of K-measures and their extensions is the most natural, it is possible, and sometimes very convenient, to use a different approach. This is to regard a random function $x(t)$ as a function of a random variable ω in some probability space Ω, and this is particularly convenient if it turns out that Ω can be taken to be one of the familiar spaces such as the unit interval.

For example, we get a random function in this way by defining

$$x(t) = x(\omega, t) = \omega_1 \cos t + \omega_2 \cos 2t \ldots + \omega_n \cos nt,$$

where $\omega = (\omega_1, \omega_2, \ldots, \omega_n)$ is a random real n-vector. A random function defined in this way for all t will define a unique K-measure, and will obviously be an extension of it. But it will not be the only extension and may not necessarily be the most useful one.

In the last resort, a random function can always be treated in this way by means of the identity function over the function space $\mathscr{X}$ itself with the measure already defined in it. Apart from convenience of notation, there seems to be little advantage in this.

The classification of random functions by the properties of their measures is one of the basic problems of the theory, and we can go no further here than to introduce some of the ideas on which useful classifications have been made. It is important in all cases to recognise whether the property of the measure can be expressed as a property of its underlying K-measure or not.

First, a random function is called **stationary** if the transformation of $\mathscr{X}$ on to itself defined by the translation $x(t) \to x(t+a)$ is measure-preserving in the sense that any measurable set is transformed into a measurable set of the same measure. The property is plainly related to the measure itself, and not merely to its K-measure. Thus a K-measure may be stationary, while an extension of it is not.

A random function is said to have **independent increments** if the random numbers $x(t_i') - x(t_i)$ are independent for every finite set of non-overlapping intervals (t_i, t_i'). This property also relates only to the K-measure and its generating distributions. The following theorem shows how these can be expressed in a convenient and characteristic form.

The theory is a natural extension of that for series of independent random variables, and is closely related, as we should expect, to the central limit theorem and the theory of infinitely divisible distributions.

THEOREM 33. (i) *If $x(t)$ is a stationary random function with independent increments, and if $\phi_h(u)$ is the characteristic function of $x(t+h) - x(t)$ and $\phi_\varepsilon(u) \to 1$ as $\varepsilon \to 0$ then $\phi_h(u) = e^{h\psi(u)}$, where $\psi(u)$ is a K-L function which does not depend on t or h.* (ii) *Conversely, any function $\phi_h(u)$ of this form is the characteristic function of $x(t+x) - x(t)$ for some stationary random functions with independent increments.*

To prove (i), we note that $\phi_h(u) = \{\phi_{h/n}(u)\}^n$ for any positive h and n and $\phi_h(n)$ is therefore infinitely divisible and has the form $e^{\psi(h, u)}$ by

H

Theorem 18.   Moreover, since $\phi_{h+\varepsilon} = \phi_h\phi_\varepsilon$ and $\phi_\varepsilon \to 1$ as $\varepsilon \to 0$, it follows that $\psi(h, u)$ is continuous in h and the identity

$$\psi(h, u) = n\psi(h/n, u)$$

is enough to show that

$$\psi(h, u) = h\psi(1, u) = h\psi(u).$$

The converse is obvious from the way in which $\phi_h(u)$ defines a system of generating distributions which plainly have the form needed for a stationary function with independent increments.

A random function is said to be an L_2 **function** if, for every fixed t, $x(t)$ is an L_2 function over $\mathscr{X}$ with respect to its probability measure in $\mathscr{X}$. The whole process can then be described as a trajectory or curve, with parameter t, in the Hilbert space $L_2(\mathscr{X})$, and many of its properties can be described in terms of the **auto-correlation function**:

$$r(s, t) = \overline{r(t, s)} = E\{[x(s)-m(s)]\overline{[x(t)-m(t)]}\}$$
$$= E\{x(s)\overline{x(t)}\} - m(s)\overline{m(t)},$$

where $m(t) = E\{x(t)\}$ is the mean over $\mathscr{X}$ of the value of the function at t.   Since the mean $m(t)$ is defined for all t, we can consider the random function $x(t)-m(t)$, which has mean 0 for every t, and is said to be **centred**.   A particularly important type of L_2 function is the **Gaussian**, for which the generating distributions are all normal and are defined completely by the autocorrelation function.

A random function whose increments over non-overlapping intervals are uncorrelated is said to have **orthogonal increments** or to be an **orthogonal L_2-random function**.   The necessary and sufficient condition for this when the function is centred is that

$$E\{[x(t')-x(t)]\overline{[x(s')-x(s)]}\} = 0$$

when the intervals (t, t') and (s, s') do not overlap.   This can be put in the form

$$E\{|\,[x(t')-x(t)] + [x(s')-x(s)]\,|^2\}$$
$$= E\{|\,x(t')-x(t)\,|^2\} + E\{|\,x(s')-x(s)\,|^2\},$$

which means that

$$E\{|\,x(t')-x(t)\,|^2\} = F(t')-F(t)$$

for some non-decreasing function $F(t)$ and every t, t'.

The autocorrelation function may be used to define a weaker form of the stationary property.   We say that $x(t)$ is **stationary in the L_2-sense** if $r(s, t)$ depends only on $t-s$, and this implies that $r(t, t+h) = \rho(h)$ and $F(t+h)-F(t) = h\sigma^2$ for some positive σ.

It is plain that the properties of L_2 functions which have been mentioned, and all other properties that can be expressed in terms of its autocorrelation function, are properties of its K-measure and are equally true of any extension of it.

Apart from the problem associated with the classification of random functions and the study of special types, there are two more fundamental problems. First, the *separability* problem is that of expressing properties of random functions in terms of countable sets of conditions. This is desirable since the presentation of measurability and probability conditions is generally limited to countable sequences of operations.

The second problem is that of determining conditions under which a random function $x(t)$, regarded as a real valued function on the product space $\mathscr{X} \otimes \mathscr{T}$, is *measurable* with respect to the product of the probability measure in $\mathscr{X}$ and Lebesgue or Stieltjes measure in $\mathscr{T}$. It is plainly essential to establish measurability in this sense in order to develop a natural theory of integration to embrace both integration in $\mathscr{X}$, as in the L_2 theory mentioned above, and the integration in $\mathscr{T}$ of individual or sample functions $x(t)$.

A general discussion of these two problems is beyond the scope of this book and an interested reader should refer to Doob† and the periodical literature. The most that can be attempted here is to show how the problems can be discussed by *ad hoc* methods in two important special cases.

THEOREM 34 (*The Brownian or Wiener Process*). *A stationary random function with independent increments can be defined in such a way that $x(0) = 0$, the distribution of $x(t+h) - x(t)$ is normal $(0, h\sigma^2)$ and $x(t)$ is continuous in t with probability* 1.

There is plainly no loss of generality in assuming that $\sigma = 1$. We consider first the set $\mathscr{T}_0$ of rationals and deduce from Theorem 25 that a probability measure μ_0 can be established in the space $\mathscr{X}_0$ of real valued functions over $\mathscr{T}_0$ in such a way that $x(0) = 0$ and the increments over intervals $(t, t+h)$ are normal $(0, h)$ when t and $t+h$ are in $\mathscr{T}_0$ and are independent for non-overlapping intervals.

The first step is to prove that functions on $\mathscr{T}_0$ are continuous in $\mathscr{T}_0$ with probability 1 with respect to this measure. Let

$$\varepsilon > 0, \quad t = t_0 < t_1 \ldots < t_n = t + \delta,$$

and let k be the first integer in $1 \leq k \leq n$ for which $x(t_k) - x(t_0) \geq \varepsilon$.

---

† J. L. DOOB, *Stochastic Processes*, New York, 1953.

The integer k is a function of x in $\mathcal{X}_0$, and is therefore a random integer, and we have

$$P\left\{\sup_{1\leq v\leq n}[x(t_v)-x(t_0)]\geq\varepsilon\right\}-P\{x(t_n)-x(t_0)\geq\varepsilon\}$$

$$=\sum_{v=1}^{n-1}P\{k=v,\ x(t_n)-x(t_0)<\varepsilon\}\leq\sum_{v=1}^{n-1}P\{k=v,\ x(t_n)-x(t_v)<0\}$$

$$=\sum_{v=1}^{n-1}P\{k=v,\ x(t_n)-x(t_v)>0\},$$

since increments all have symmetrical distributions, and this does not exceed

$$\sum_{v=1}^{n}P\{k=v,\ x(t_n)-x(t_0)\geq\varepsilon\}\leq P\{x(t_n)-x(t_0)\geq\varepsilon\}.$$

If we combine this with a similar inequality for

$$P\left\{\sup_{1\leq v\leq n}[x(t_v)-x(t_0)]\leq-\varepsilon\right\},$$

we get

$$P\left\{\sup_{1\leq v\leq n}|x(t_v)-x(t_0)|\geq\varepsilon\right\}\leq 2P\{|x(t+\delta)-x(t)|\geq\varepsilon\}$$

$$=2(2/\pi)^{\frac{1}{2}}\int_{\varepsilon/\delta^{1/2}}^{\infty}e^{-u^2/2}du\leq 2(2\delta/\pi\varepsilon^2)^{\frac{1}{2}}e^{-\varepsilon^2/2\delta}.$$

Since this holds for all finite sets of points t_i of $\mathcal{T}_0$, the same inequality holds if the expression on the left is replaced by

$$P\left\{\sup_{t\leq t'\leq t+\delta}|x(t')-x(t)|\geq\varepsilon\right\}.$$

Hence, if N is a positive integer, and I is an interval of length N^{-1}

$$P\left\{\sup_{t,\ t'\varepsilon I_nT_0}|x(t')-x(t)|\geq 2N^{-\frac{1}{2}+\alpha}\right\}\leq 4N^{-\alpha}e^{-N^{2\alpha}/2},$$

and we deduce that there is probability less than $8AN^{1-\alpha}e^{-N^{2\alpha}/2}$ that $|x(t')-x(t)|\geq 2N^{-1/2+\varepsilon}$ for any rational points t, t' in the interval $[-A,\ A]$ which satisfy $|t'-t|\leq 1/N$. Since $\Sigma N^{-\alpha}e^{-N^{2\alpha}/2}$ converges, it follows that $|x(t')-x(t)|=0\{|t'-t|^{1/2-\varepsilon}\}$ uniformly in $-A\leq t,\ t'\leq A$ as $t'-t\to 0$ with probability as near as we please to 1, and this property, which implies continuity, must therefore hold with probability 1.

We now have a measure μ_0 in $\mathcal{X}_0$ with the property that almost all functions of $\mathcal{X}_0$ are continuous in $\mathcal{T}_0$. Since there is a one to one correspondence between the continuous function in $\mathscr{X}_0$ and the continuous function of $\mathscr{X}$, the measure μ_0 defines a probability measure in the subspace $\mathscr{X}_1$ of continuous functions of $\mathscr{X}$. We complete the definition of the required probability measure μ in $\mathscr{X}$ by defining the measurable sets X of $\mathscr{X}$ to be those for which $X \cap \mathscr{X}_1$, is measurable with respect to μ_1. It is clear that these form a σ-ring on which μ, defined by $\mu(X) = \mu_1(X \cap \mathscr{X}_1)$, is a probability measure. The set of all functions on $\mathscr{T}$ with a discontinuity has no element in common with $\mathscr{X}_1$ and therefore has measure 0.

Since μ is derived from conditions on the values of the functions at points of $\mathscr{T}_0$, it is not immediately obvious that μ is an extension of the K-measure defined by the given generating distribution in the space $\mathscr{X}$ of functions defined over the whole line $\mathscr{T}$. This follows, however, if we note that the conditions of the form $a \leq x(t) < b$ which define the simple sets in $\mathscr{X}$ can all be expressed in terms of a countable number of similar conditions at points of $\mathscr{T}_0$. The simple sets are then measurable with respect to μ_1 and therefore with respect to its extension μ. In particular, the increments $x(t+h) - x(t)$ are normal $(0, h)$ for all real t and h and are independent over non-overlapping intervals.

THEOREM 35 (*The Poisson Process*). *A stationary random function with independent increments can be defined in such a way that $x(0) = 0$ and the increment $x(t+h) - x(t)$ has Poisson distribution with mean hc and $x(t)$ is, with probability* 1, *a non-decreasing step function with a finite number of discontinuities of magnitude* 1 *in any finite interval.*

We proceed as in the last theorem to define a random function in the space $\mathscr{X}_0$ of functions defined over the set $\mathscr{T}_0$ of rationals. With respect to this measure, $P\{x(t+h) < x(t)\} = 0$ for any fixed t and h and it follows that, with probability 1, $x(t+h) \geq x(t)$ for all t, h in $\mathscr{T}_0$. Moreover, again with probability 1, $x(t)$ takes only positive or zero integral values and is therefore a step function, with positive integral discontinuities. But

$$P\{x(t+h) - x(t) \geq 2\} = e^{-ch} \sum_{v=2}^{\infty} \frac{(ch)^v}{v!} \leq c^2 h^2$$

for any fixed t, h, and the probability that $x(t)$ has a discontinuity of magnitude greater than 1 in $-A \leq t \leq A$ does not exceed the probability that in at least one of the N intervals of length $2A/N$ into which it can be divided its increment will be at least 2, and this probability is less than $NC^2(2A/N)^2 = O(1/N)$. This is arbitrarily small by choice of N, and the probability that $x(t)$ will have a discontinuity greater than 1 must be 0.

The remaining argument is similar to that used in Theorem 34. Every step function in $\mathscr{X}_0$ defines uniquely a step function of the required type in $\mathscr{X}$, and we have therefore a probability measure μ_1 over the subspace $\mathscr{X}_1$ of $\mathscr{X}$ consisting of these step functions. The extension of μ_1 to a measure μ over the whole of $\mathscr{X}$ then follows as before, and it is plain that the simple functions in $\mathscr{X}$ are again measurable with respect to μ, which is therefore an extension of K-measure.

The properties of the individual function $x(t)$ can be expressed in terms of the distances λ_1, λ_2, ... between successive discontinuities, and the following theorem gives the form of this random sequence.

THEOREM 36. *Suppose that $x(t)$ is a Poisson random function and that the discontinuities of a typical sample function are at λ_1, $\lambda_1+\lambda_2$, $\lambda_1+\lambda_2+\lambda_3$, ... Then λ_1, λ_2, ... are independent random real numbers and each has probability density $ce^{-c\lambda}$ in $\lambda > 0$.*

The probability that the first discontinuity lies in the interval (t_1, t_1+h_1) is

$$P\{x(t_1)-x(0) = 0, \quad x(t_1+h_1)-x(t_1) = 1\}$$
$$= e^{-ct_1}e^{-ch_1}ch_1 = ch_1\{e^{-ct_1}+o(1)\} \text{ as } h_1 \to 0.$$

Since this is continuous in t_1, it follows that

$$P\{t_1 \leq \lambda_1 < t_1+h_1 \dots t_n \leq \lambda_n < t_n+h_n\} = c^h h_1 h_2 \dots h_n e^{-c(t_1+t_2 \dots +t_n)}[1+o(1)]$$

for small h_1, h_2, ..., h_n, and this is sufficient.

It is clear in the two examples discussed that the sample functions are almost all measurable in t and the question of their measurability in the product space $\mathscr{X} \otimes \mathscr{T}$ can also be treated in a simple way. In the Poisson case, we have to show that the set in $\mathscr{X} \otimes \mathscr{T}$ for which $0 \leq x(t) < n$ for a given non-negative integer n is measurable, and this is obvious if we note that the set can be defined by $0 \leq t < \Lambda_n(x)$ for every x in $\mathscr{X}$, where $\Lambda_n(x)$ is the distance from 0 of the n-th discontinuity of x and is measurable over $\mathscr{X}$.

In the Brownian case, it is sufficient to show that the set $\mathscr{E}\{x(t) < b\}$ in $\mathscr{X} \otimes \mathscr{T}$ can be approximated by measurable sets of the form $X_i \otimes T_i$, where T_i is an interval $(t_i \leq t < t_{i+1})$ and X_i is the subset of $\mathscr{X}$ for which $x(t_i) < b$.

SUGGESTIONS FOR FURTHER READING

BARTLETT, M. S. *Stochastic Processes*, Cambridge (1955).

BLANC-LAPIERRE, A. and FORTET, R. *Theorie des fonctions aléatoires*, Paris (1953).

CRAMÉR, H. *Mathematical Methods of Statistics*, Princeton (1951).

DOOB, J. L. *Stochastic Processes*, New York (1953).

FELLER, W. *An introduction to Probability Theory and its applications*, New York, Second Edition (1957).

GNEDENKO and KOLMOGOROFF, A. N. *Limit distribution for Sums of Independent Random Variables* (with additional appendix by K. L. Chung and J. L. Doob), Cambridge, Mass. (1954).

HALMOS, P. R. *Measure Theory*, New York (1953).

KHINTCHINE, A. *Asymptotische Gesetze der Wahrscheinlichkeitsrechrung*, (Ergebn. Math. 2, No. 4) (1933).

KOLMOGOROFF, A. N. *Grundbegriffe der Wahrscheinlichkeitsrechrung*, Berlin (1933). (English translation, New York (1950)).

LÉVY, P. *Processus Stochastiques et Mouvement Brownien*, Paris (1948).

LOÈVE, M. *Probability Theory*, New York, Second Edition (1960).

WIENER, N. *The extrapolation, interpolation and smoothing of Stationary Time-series*, New York (1949).

INDEX

PRINTED IN GREAT BRITAIN BY
OLIVER AND BOYD LTD.
EDINBURGH